MAGIC MEDICINE

HOMEOPATHY AS SHAMANISM

To Karen —
Be Blessed
Be Magic
Be Well
Gloria D.

BOOKS BY GLORIA ST JOHN

From Doctor to Healer: The Transformative Journey
(with Robbie Davis-Floyd)

Ashes, Ashes, We All Fall Down:
Becoming a Devotee of Sathya Sai Baba

The Way Home: A Journey through the Chakras

MAGIC MEDICINE

HOMEOPATHY AS SHAMANISM

Gloria St. John

Coral Reef Press

Coral Reef Press

info@goldhillshomeopathy.com

Printed in the United States of America
First printing April 2019

Painting on cover, *Quando las Plantas Cantan,* (When the Plants Sing) by Luis Tamani luis-tamani.com
Samuel Hahnemann image on cover from the World History Archive

ISBN 978-1-7324373-1-9
Library of Congress Control Number 2019901957

Magic Medicine Homeopathy As Shamanism /
Gloria St. John. —1st ed.
Includes index.

1. Alternative Medicine. 2. Samuel Hahnemann. 3. Homeopathy. 4. Shamanism. 5. Natural Health. 6. Magic.

To Homeopaths and Shamans worldwide

~~~~ May your light shine brightly
~~~~

CONTENTS

~~~~~ I've often slept out on the water.
Late, very late, as you're rocked into slumber,
you'll hear your heart pumping blood through
your body, and even later, if you're still enough,
you'll hear the low hum of your chakras as life
force flows through you, and later still
you'll hear the grinding of the constellations
lumbering across the heavens.

September with Purple Horse Woman,
~~ Tienne Beaulieu
~~~~~

Foreword

Gloria St John is inviting us through a doorway that opens an exciting new perspective into the profound connection between two of the most successful healing methods on the planet: Homeopathy and Shamanism.

Samuel Hahnemann, the originator of homeopathy, was a powerful shaman. He had the vision to create one of the most highly organized, astonishingly effective and gentle, non-invasive systems of healing ever known to man. He made homeopathic medicines by mixing parts of a plant, mineral or animal with water and then shaking and diluting it repeatedly until no original source of the substance could be found. So it became a very tiny dose that had no toxic effect. Like a shaman, he then asked the substance how it would heal the patient.

He did this by conducting provings where he gave the substance to healthy people, and then asked them to detail what their new symptoms were. These symptoms then became a detailed repertory of what that particular plant or animal could heal. He had the profound insight (though he did not know it at the time) that water holds memory.

This "insight" is being proved by some of the greatest scientists of today such as Nobel laureate Dr. Luc Montagnier. The struggle is that the concept that water holds memory, though provable by scientific method, is beyond the belief system of most linear-minded scientists. Despite Montagnier's (and others) proof, most modern scientists refuse to consider the possibility.

We, "shamanic homeopaths," as Gloria so aptly describes us, can seek Mother Nature's wisdom in the form of a water-diluted vial of cobra venom or *Bellis perennis* (daisy) or a fragment of gold bullion. It all looks like the same little white pellets, but each is significantly different. The remedies hold the essence or memory of the animal, plant or mineral inside of them. We take the case of the patient and match it as closely as possible to the exact symptoms and temperament of one of our remedies. Then we give them that remedy.

Homeopathy utilizes the earth and all its denizens - be they plant, animal or mineral - as its wisest teachers and healers. Our colleagues, the Tibetan, Native American, South American or African shamans, use all of the earth's gifts as well, albeit in a totally different manner. How homeopaths are so similar yet different from shamans is the subject of this most fascinating book. Both these methods of healing have remained shrouded in mystery.

In the 200 years since its origin, the system of homeopathy has not seen any basic changes in its core principles. This is the sign of something that is true. Truth does not change with the times. Truth remains true.

Since homeopathy was developed, no one has understood how these magic elixirs can stop a severe migraine headache in moments, can take away the agony of a finger slammed in a car door in a second, or restore joy to a depressed person.

While in Africa with my husband, Roger Morrison, we met with a small group of shamans. As we sat and talked, the beautiful white trumpet flowers of the Datura plant were all around us. We told them, "We use these plants for healing."

They were astounded! "In Africa that plant is only used for killing. It is very dangerous," they said. "Do not use it!" We said: "We give it all the time to children who have nightmares and to people in a state of terror, fearing that they might be murdered. It can cure their fear in one dose. Our form of diluted medicine makes everything safe - even the most horrific poisons."

Thank you so much Gloria for elucidating this powerful connection for us and for illustrating it so vividly through your many examples. The world of medicine, struggling to be "scientific and evidence-based," has not been ready for this book until now, but I believe the time has come.

All blessings on this exciting new endeavor.

Nancy Herrick MA, PA, DH (H)
Hahnemann Medical Clinic,
Richmond, California

Preface

How Homeopathy Healed Me

The touch of the fairy godmother's wand on Cinderella's shoulder transformed her from a rag-clad, grimy servant to a woman ready for the ball and the prince.

Thirty years ago, I was like Cinderella, psychically feeding on ashes. I had chronic fatigue syndrome—a simultaneous collapse of many organs and systems that pulls the plug on energy, vitality, and enthusiasm, and makes it impossible to function normally. No amount of sleep restored me. I lay on the sofa day after day, for weeks and months, trying to tend to my two-year-old son, praying he would nap soon and for a long time. I could not do the simplest errand such as go to a convenience store and buy one item. I could not lift my son into his car seat. I could not walk across a parking lot. I longed for a handicap permit. I wanted to die rather than continue to live this way.

I did not go to a doctor. I was quite sure that I had chronic fatigue and I knew, from friends who suffered from similar symptoms, that the current medication prescribed for chronic fatigue was toxic to the liver and helped only minimally in most cases. A neighbor who visited one day wisely observed that I should do something. She suggested I go to the Hahnemann Clinic in Berkeley (where I lived). She told me that there were "people there who used alternative treatments of some type." Maybe it would help me. My inner voice said to give it a try.

How had I become so ill, so depleted? Life was good. My husband and I had just realized a long-held dream of moving from Chicago to California. We had a nice home, reveled in the weather, and adored our son. I needed to look back in time to discover the roots of this collapse.

A proximate cause was the homebirth of my son two years earlier, when both my newborn son and I nearly died, and we would have, if it had not been for the skill of the attending physician and midwife. The specter of death hungrily walked through that birthing bedroom where I had anticipated only joy and new life. I never allowed myself to feel the fear of dying and the pain of leaving my newborn on earth without his mother. I went on as though this were only a small glitch in the overall plan, wryly referring to the experience as "the homebirth from hell." Instead I became absorbed in the joy of our new family and caring for my baby. Apparently fear I felt got stuck inside me somewhere.

Before my re-marriage and son's birth, I spent many years as a single parent to my two older daughters. During this time I managed a household, supported the family, acquired two masters' degrees, and travelled as a consultant for a fascinating job in public health. Although I always felt that I was juggling way too many balls at one time, I never collapsed during this period. It is well known in medical circles that collapse often follows periods of stress: after one has borne up mightily, everything can fall apart. And I was in pieces.

The onset of my fatigue symptoms was very sudden and specific. They descended on me on August 16th and 17th in 1987, days known in new age and astrological circles as the Harmonic Convergence. What was the Harmonic Convergence?

> The Harmonic Convergence was celebrated worldwide by tens of thousands if not millions of people and marked the first time human beings simultaneously coordinated their prayers, meditations, and ceremonies at sacred sites around the planet. This was the first manifestation of a networked thrust toward a unified moment of collective synchronization. Everyone from Shirley MacLaine to Timothy Leary to John Denver celebrated the event....Many people reported significant shifts in consciousness and a reorientation in their life patterns. (*event.chronicle.com*)

Indeed my life pattern was significantly reoriented, but not in a way I would have chosen. Living in Berkeley, I was aware of the Harmonic Convergence, and I felt vaguely uneasy that I was not observing it in some way. Instead my husband and I were enjoying a weekend of biking and beach walking in Marin County. I had been aware of a growing tension in my life between the rather conventional life I was living and the possibility of living a more metaphysical and spiritually oriented life. Something or someone was about to help me resolve this tension, but in a rather painful way. One spiritual teacher said that if we are not ready to learn life lessons through joy, then we will learn through pain.

Much later I concluded that my symptoms—extreme tiredness, headaches, and the sense that an inner window shade had been pulled down in the front of my head—were like the blows that Zen masters give their students to encourage their awakening.

> "Such blows, however deceptive or harsh they might seem, are always said in the end to be informed by wisdom and motivated by compassion." (*tricycle.org*)

Pulling myself out of my bed of pain and lassitude, I made an appointment with Nancy Herrick and drove the few blocks to the Hahnemann Clinic. That I chose Nancy was completely random; I just chose someone with a name I liked from the list of practitioners. I had no idea what to expect or what the process would entail. I had a vague idea about homeopathy as the use of small doses of medicine in pills to cure. However, I did not do any research or study the method before the appointment. You see, I, who had always been lively, energetic, engaged, and curious, simply did not give a damn. My fatigue penetrated my entire system—body, mind, emotions, and spirit.

Nancy interviewed me for some time. This is a process I, now a trained homeopath, know very well. At the time, however, I had no idea what was going on. She asked me a lot of questions while she looked through books. I recall feeling envious of her stylish attire and her vitality —things I thought were beyond the pale for me forever. I asked her if she thought I had chronic fatigue syndrome. She said that names of illnesses were not as important to her as their symptoms. I asked her if she thought I would get well. She said she would do her best to help me, but could make no promises.

She prescribed a homeopathic remedy, in a high potency, to be taken one time only. I was able to purchase the remedy for under $20 right there at the pharmacy, and I took it right away. She told me to give up coffee, which I was drinking virtually all day in hopes of generating more energy. I gave it up immediately and switched to black tea. We made an appointment for me to return in about a month. Ok, I thought, here we go.

That night at home, as I was walking from one room to another, I had a very penetrating thought. "Perhaps I will not get well and will spend the rest of my life on the sofa; even so, it will be my life, and I will make something of it." I flashed on Elizabeth Barrett Browning, a lifelong invalid, who is often pictured sitting by the fire on a fainting couch writing poetry, as she is tended by her husband, poet Robert Browning. Well, that is something to ponder, I thought. My next thought was really amazing: "I no longer want to die." I knew that true healing begins in the mind, as does illness, and I gave thanks for this release from the death wish. The death wish, is, after all, a very serious—if not the greatest—disease. Two weeks later my symptoms were all gone, and I was joyfully pushing my son on a swing at the local park. In thirty years, those symptoms have never returned.

Many readers will want to know what was in those magic pills in the hope of finding that remedy and relieving their own fatigue and depression. Homeopathy is an individualized treatment; it treats the person not the illness. I responded completely to the nature spirit in the remedy prescribed for me. A person with similar symptoms will also respond to the nature spirit that will heal them, but it will probably be a different remedy. If I had known about Shamanism, I might have found someone trained in that form of healing who could have helped me. There are western shamans, and perhaps some of them practiced in the Bay Area at that time. But I was surely too ill to have made the trip to South America to experience shamans there. But, I knew nothing about Shamanism.

Through Nancy's skill, the healing power of nature came to me and made me well. This miracle is something I am sure she and other homeopaths (myself included) have witnessed many times over. Ten years later, I began training as a homeopath, and Nancy was one of my inspired teachers. I was also able to edit her book, *Animal Minds, Human Voices*, a book describing how animals speak through the process of homeopathic research, called provings. Only recently was I struck by the prophetic title —one that overtly links homeopathy and Shamanism, although I had been aware of the book for decades.

Was I one hundred percent healed on every level after this one-time treatment? While I was now physically strong again and symptom free, I still suffered from occasional depression and sadness of unknown origin. After I healed from chronic fatigue syndrome, I needed to experience and process a lot of painful events from my past, and homeopathic healing gave me the awareness and motivation to undertake this.

There are so many ways to become healthier and more integrated; life offers a smorgasbord of techniques that can take us higher and higher into our true nature and closer to our destiny. I found an astrologer who was also a psychotherapist who knew how to help me understand my Piscean nature that revels in symbols and signs and spirit and mystery. It became clear that no other approach would have worked as well for me. Since then, I have taken many steps on my healing journey, and I am grateful for all the teachers and healers who helped me.

It is from this depth of gratitude that I write this book to help reveal how the power of nature is encoded within the deceptively simple medicine of homeopathy; how the call of the sick one and the response from nature is mediated by the homeopath/shaman. It is my hope that readers will come to see, and perhaps experience firsthand, the power of homeopathy. We homeopaths are waiting to serve them.

Introduction

> Homeopathy contains the primary elements of Shamanism, but in a veiled way. Homeopaths, who practice the art, are shamans in their own right.

If ever a discipline needed branding, it is homeopathy. This powerful but arcane art and science is less understood by the general public than any other form of healing. One wonders how acupuncture, the esoteric equal of homeopathy, has become mainstreamed, licensed, adopted within HMOs, and practiced by medical doctors. Homeopathy missed the branding boat big time. When I offer classes in the use of homeopathy for acute conditions, many of the eager students who show up believe they will be hearing about herbs, nutrition, or essential oils.

What exactly is branding? Personally, I think the term is over used. According to marketing experts, every mom-and-pop hair salon needs to be branded in order to succeed. The following information from *entrepreur.com* helps clarify the essential features of branding.

> Simply put, your brand is your promise to your customer. It tells them what they can expect from your products and services, and it differentiates your offering from that of your competitors. Your brand is derived from who you are, who you want to be and who people perceive you to be.

Branding has been successful in communicating the features of many well-known products. Two auto brands, Honda and Toyota, are known for at least three features: low gas mileage, few repairs, and a long life—often over 200,000 miles. They are definitely not sporty, or classy, or ego-boosting cars. They have traded these features for economy and have become leaders in the industry. Most importantly, they continue to deliver on these three qualities through various models and over time. If someone tells you they just bought a Honda, your mind reflexively associates this person with good sense, frugality, and good judgment. If you are a sports-car enthusiast, you can still appreciate the Honda and Toyota qualities, although you would never drive such a boring car.

The importance of branding is that the name of the product or service alone communicates qualities about it. The term 'homeopathy' communicates very little, and often communicates the wrong information. The public does not understand or appreciate homeopathy; many people confuse the term with the word "holistic." Even though most people do not understand the etheric body and chi points treated by acupuncturists, they submit to the tiny needles much more readily than to a homeopathic remedy. I have pondered this knowledge gap for many years, and I have tried to counteract it with my own practice of homeopathy, as well as my teaching and writing.

After many years of searching for the right words, I have concluded that homeopathy has no "elevator speech" —the thing you say in 15 seconds when someone asks you what you do. "I practice a form of natural medicine that is made from dilute (a code word that folks don't understand) substances in nature to bring about profound healing." "Oh, you mean like herbs?" asks my eager listener. "No, remedies can be made from plant, animal, or mineral substances," I delightfully proclaim. Now the listener broods on images of dead animals (animal experimentation) or how unpleasant it would be to chew on a rock as a route to health. While I have proudly differentiated my practice from herbal medicine, I have inadvertently provided a couple of possibly horrifying images. "Oh, nice for you," a polite person will say and promptly walk away. "Would you like my brochure?" "Maybe later" (code for never).

How can a form of medicine that has been in existence for nearly 250 years be so obscure and misunderstood? How is it that many, if not most, educated Americans have never heard of it (nor can they pronounce the name correctly after hearing it)? Even those who have heard of it have misconceptions galore. While it is easy to blame the smear-campaign of conventional medicine—which claims that homeopathy is either a placebo or poison—there is more at work here.

Homeopathy is hard to understand and even harder to explain. It is full of idiosyncrasies and is unique in so many ways. We homeopaths treasure the little peculiarities that are part of our art. We like the Latin names of our medicines, which we call remedies. In fact, an entire glossary of terms is needed by most people even to begin to understand the terms we use, let alone how the process works.

One particularly difficult fact is that the more dilute the substance in a remedy (weaker in normal terms), the stronger (more potent in homeo-speak) is the remedy. This is a mind-bender to most. Then there are the "potencies" expressed not just in numbers but in numbers with letters. For example there is 30X and then there is 30C. How are they related—or are they?

I love to demystify these confusing aspects of homeopathy when I teach, but few people have access to such information. We live in an age of expediency. We want things that are easy-to-understand, easy-to-obtain, easy-to-use, and are effective.

The saddest part of my teaching is that I am just skimming the surface when I teach the use of remedies for first aid. I have to mentally sit on my hands to resist talking about kingdoms and miasms, the imponderables, and all the juicy concepts that make practicing homeopathy so rich. But who cares about these things? Not many people. Most people want to go to the health food store; find the darn stuff (carefully displayed in a manner unlike any other medicinal item); select the best medicine (a task confounded by the "indications" written on the tubes); get the proper strength for their condition (no clear guidance here); and feel better after they take the stuff (once they figure out how to get the little pills out of the bottle).

The sad, or perhaps exciting, part is that they can feel much better almost immediately if they even get close to the correct remedy and potency. And it won't cost much either. Remedies are sold for less than ten dollars in most locations. Along the way, they will be avoiding immune-compromising substances such as antibiotics, cortisone, and pain killers and, at the same time, strengthening their vital force (another term we like). Additionally, this enhanced vital force will stand them in good stead the next time they are ill or injured.

And how innocuous this medicine appears! Little pills that all look alike whether they contain snake venom or chamomile. How can that be? Then, they taste pretty good, dissolve well, and travel easily. Most of this cannot be said of many of the foul-smelling and bitter-tasting herbs prescribed by acupuncturists, for example.

So after decades of trying to unwind homeopathy by diving into it—remedies are medicines; potency is strength; less is more; dilute is strong, Latin is fun!—I decided to build a bridge to a sexier and more vibrant system—Shamanism.

If you mention the word "Shamanism" to almost anyone, they will have a clear image. Even if it is erroneous, something comes to mind. This may be a jungle scene, a person clad in feathers, dancing, some smoke, or chants. This is a lot of material to get from one word: a scene, a person, action, a scent, and a sound. "Homeopathy," on the other hand, conjures absolutely nothing to most people. And yet (and you will need to trust me on this at this point), *homeopathy is as powerful in its colorless, quiet, and obscure way, as Shamanism.* In fact, it operates in precisely the same way as Shamanism, by harnessing specific natural forces for healing.

Ask about Shamanism and the words you will hear are "ancient, exotic, foreign, mysterious, sexy, primitive, and powerful." People will give a little involuntary psychic shudder because they just know somehow that Shamanism is true, even if they have not experienced it. And, they also wish they could experience it—but shamans are so hard to find (they think), and jungles so dangerous. Maybe, some day....

So let's revisit the elevator. "What do you do?" "I practice a form of modern-day Shamanism to heal people." "Wow! That sounds interesting!" And it also sounds exotic and powerful. My listener is engaged: "Where do you do this?" or "How did you learn it?" "You're kidding, right?" But something ensues to open a conversation; and they will take my brochure.

I want you to know that the shaman of your dreams is in the elevator with you, but he or she will probably not reveal that, because, for the most part, homeopaths do not even know that they are shamans. Homeopathy contains the primary elements of Shamanism, but in a veiled way. And, homeopaths, who practice the art, are shamans in their own right.

I want to introduce you to the elements of Shamanism —the shaman, the trance, the journey, the ancestors, and the nature spirits—and show how each of these is central to the practice of homeopathy. You don't need a drum or a rattle, nor do you need to chant; but I promise you will feel the power in this art as it commands the forces of nature to heal.

CHAPTER ONE

Homeopathy and Shamanism Origins and Methods

Homeopaths are shamanistic in their ability to find the relationship between the suffering person and the substance in nature that will heal that person.

The Founding of Homeopathy

Samuel Hahnemann was a German medical doctor, scholar, chemist, and master of many languages who founded homeopathy. He fathered 11 children, was dogged by poverty, and was criticized by conventional doctors of the time, whose brutal practices he condemned. He railed against the practice of emetics, bloodletting, and other techniques he considered barbaric, as well as the use of mercury and quinine in treating illness. Naturally this did not make him popular with his medical and pharmaceutical contemporaries.

Samuel Hahnemann
1755-1843

A statement he made in the *Organon*, quoted below, makes it clear that he did not mince words! It might be pointed out that some of the same accusations he made then are being used today to describe conventional medicine.

> The adherents of the old school of medicine assail the body with large, often protracted and rapidly repeated doses of strong medicine, whose long lasting and not infrequently terrible effects they do not know.... The long employment of such formulas inflicts new, and in part, ineradicable medicinal

> diseases on the sick body. This is a very easy business, once one has got the knack of this ruinous procedure and has become properly insensitive to the warnings of conscience. [p.2]

After the death of his first wife, Hahnemann found solace and happiness in a second marriage to a much younger woman, who played a major role in developing, protecting, and preserving his work. His major work, the *Organon of Medicine*, contains both the philosophy and the practical application of homeopathic practice. He wrote six editions of this classic, with the final edition finally published in 1922. The term "organon," though out-of-date now, means "a set of principles."

It is rare, perhaps unprecedented, for such a complex, complete, and effective healing system to be developed by only one person. More unique, perhaps, is the fact that homeopathy is practiced today, at least in its classical form, in the same manner that Hahnemann prescribed. While Hahnemann developed more than 90 remedies in his lifetime, there are now about 5000 remedies in use. Some of his original remedies are stored in the rare-books section of the library at the University of California in San Francisco, along with the fifth edition of the *Organon*. These remedies that Hahnemann himself prepared have been sampled by leading homeopaths and found to be effective today - 200 years after they were made. Homeopathic remedies that are well cared for never expire—contrary to the FDA's insistence that each medicine carry an expiration date on its packaging.

A homeopathic remedy is energy medicine disguised in little pills, sometimes as a liquid. This is perhaps one of the most confounding aspects of homeopathy. When asked about energy medicine, many people think of Reiki, hands-on healing, or therapeutic touch. They may even refer to energy medicine as aura reading and clearing, or medical intuitive work. Some machines, such as the Rife machine, appear to demonstrate a more direct relationship to energy than do the homeopathic remedies.

People today are all too familiar with the idea of taking a pill to feel better. It is the major therapy that is used in conventional medicine. Conventional pharmaceuticals are chemicals that alter the chemistry in the body to produce certain effects—they may suppress inflammation (steroids) or kill microorganisms (antibiotics) in the body. More sophisticated medications can affect the biochemistry and metabolic processes in more complex ways, but they are often accompanied by negative effects. Homeopathic pills, on the other hand, are dynamic. They are able to affect the body's many energetic layers—physical, mental, emotional, and spiritual—with no side effects. They pack a whammy, indeed!

I have always wondered how such a dynamic system could have originated through the work of a maverick doctor, albeit one who was well versed in the history of medicine and highly gifted in languages. His knowledge of languages generated many appointments as a translator, and he translated many texts in the scientific realm. This, surely, allowed him to become acquainted with the history of scientific thought. But a reading of the life of Hahnemann does not bring us anywhere near to "magic" or anything like it.

He was a family man, a struggling scientist, and a brilliant intellect who found it hard to find a niche in society. Not that he did not try. He tried the practices of pharmacy, medicine, teaching, tutoring, and writing. But how did he come up with his own system? What were the influences that led him to develop such an esoteric, unique, and powerful system of healing?

In a search for clues that might answer these questions, I reviewed what was written about Hahnemann's life. I found one entry that caused me to stop in my tracks. It seems that Hahnemann spent several years in the employ of the Governor of Transylvania. Now, Transylvania is a word that conjures up the possibility of magic and mystery. With its forests and roaming spirits, it evokes the sense of magic and mystery perhaps more than any other spot on earth. And what did Hahnemann do for the Governor of Transylvania? He cataloged and translated what has been described as the most extensive collection of alchemical and magical documents in Europe. In this rather peaceful appointment, he was not hounded by doctors or pharmacists, his income was adequate to support his large family, and he had time to continue his own research into the nature of substances.

I like to think of the governor and Hahnemann sitting up late, sipping brandy while the candles guttered, discussing these texts and sharing insights and questions. We all know the magical feeling of encountering a like-minded person who shares one of our esoteric interests—a friend who can help us delve more deeply into a subject and express our passion about it. I think, perhaps, this was the gift given to Hahnemann in Transylvania, and that it helped him form the basis for his medical system, making him bolder and clearer in its development.

He also became a Mason. This fraternal organization began at the end of the fourteenth century and still thrives today behind closed doors and rituals. Masonry is rich in symbols, as well as mysteries and occultism. It may have bolstered Hahnemann's interest in and knowledge about these subjects, while providing him some much-needed fraternal support.

Shamanism

There is no question that Shamanism predates homeopathy by millennia. It is the oldest known system of healing. Shamanism was first recognized by western observers working among traditional herding societies in central and northern Asia, and it is from the language of these Tungus–speaking peoples of Siberia that the term "shaman" is derived. In that language, the word is saman and means "one who is excited, moved, raised." It refers to individuals who visit, while in a trance state, the realm of mystical beings to communicate with them. One of their functions is to determine what is ailing a person and how they might be healed. They do this by journeying beyond the body to access subtle energetic realms where they may encounter and interact with nature spirits or mystical beings for the purpose of healing the sick. Sometimes these journeys are induced by hallucinogenic substances.

Although Shamanism is usually associated with early and primitive peoples, it has gained popularity in the west, and it is now possible to become a western shaman without traveling to another country – or even leaving your home. Shamanism is gaining popularity with the generally renewed recognition of the healing power of nature. Practicing Shamanism relies only on the abilities of the shaman and does not require offices, tools, medicines or any of the trappings of other modalities, although many colorful and dramatic effects may be used.

> Training in core shamanism is particularly suited to contemporary society and includes teaching students to alter their consciousness through classic shamanic non-drug techniques such as repetitive drumming so that they can discover their own hidden spiritual resources, transform their lives, and learn how to help others. (*Core Shamanism and Daily Life, December 2009,* Susan Mokelke, J.D., The Foundation for Shamanic Studies. www.shamanism.org)

In 1979, Michael and Sandra Harner established the Center for Shamanic Studies, the precursor to the Foundation for Shamanic Studies. The Foundation has taught shamanic knowledge to thousands of students through weekend and residential trainings. It has also studied and preserved information about indigenous shamanism.

Shamanism and Homeopathy

Many homeopaths have alluded to the connection between Shamanism and homeopathy in their writings, but have not made the connection explicit. Upon reflection, though, I will venture a guess that many patients and practitioners will say they have experienced Shamanism's power in their homeopathic healing.

Perhaps no homeopath has more directly referenced Shamanism than Nancy Herrick, a world renowned practitioner, lecturer, and teacher. Her two books, *Animal Minds, Human Voices* and *Sacred Plants, Human Voices*, have titles that speak directly to a link between Shamanism and homeopathy. In fairness, she did not make this link explicit. Her books are summaries of provings—the way in which new remedies are discovered and their effects tested within homeopathy. Chapter Three provides more detail about this process.

Another contemporary Indian homeopath, Rajan Sankaran, has written books titled *The Soul of Remedies* and *The Spirit of Homeopathy*; and Didier Grandgeorge, MD, has written one called *The Spirit of Homeopathic Remedies*. Edward Whitmont, MD, a Jungian analyst and homeopath, wrote classical treatises on the relationship of consciousness and homeopathy: *Psyche and Substance* and *The Alchemy of Healing: Psyche and Soma*.

These writers have described the vitality of the substances contained in homeopathic remedies. They maintain that it is the living qualities in the substances that convey healing to the sick person. Herrick actually personifies the animals and plants that she uses in her remedies. With the animal remedies, she gives voice to their contextual situation. This can include allusions to political and social issues, such as the poaching of elephants and decimation of the wolf population, which come through the consciousness of the animals affected. The provings also reflect the normal organization of animal families, such as roles, hierarchy, and care of the young.

In her books, Herrick demonstrates how each of the eight animals and seven plants she uses has a distinct imprint or set of qualities that differentiates it from the others. This is also true of the other 5000 remedies homeopaths prescribe. It is the skill, the art, of the homeopath/shaman to match the person's suffering to the correct substance in nature that will achieve a cure. To readers of this book who have neither practiced nor experienced homeopathy, all this may seem a bit abstract and erudite. The important take–away is that the shaman/homeopath recognizes an energetic signature that plants, animals, and even minerals communicate through their characteristics, and that the person who needs the remedy in some way shares those characteristics.

Michael Pollan speaks of the aliveness of a world perceived under the influence of psychedelics. Shamans would probably maintain that the perception described in the following quote is the real world, albeit, one not seen by ordinary eyes.

> ...I felt the leaves and plants in the garden returning my gaze.... Psychedelic consciousness...(grants) us a wider, more generous lens through which we can glimpse the...spirit of everything, animal, vegetable, even mineral, all of it now somehow returning our gaze. Spirits are everywhere. New rays of relation appear between us and all the world's others. (p. 413)

Many shamanic journeys include a search for the power animal that is thought to provide protection through its qualities. Cougars, lions, tigers, and the elusive snow leopard, for example, may appear to offer powers of fierceness, strength, fearlessness, and an adeptness for surviving in nature. What if one's power animal is a much more homely and less dramatic being? What if it were, say, a mollusk? Each species has its own characteristics and way of moving in the world, protecting itself and its young, finding food and shelter, and reproducing. Who is to say that the mollusk is any less dramatic in its milieu than the lion in his?

Certainly not Edward Whitmont, MD, who, in *Psyche and Substance*, provides a beautiful description of the cuttlefish, the mollusk from which the remedy *Sepia* is made, and its relationship, through its form and function, to the ideas of repression, exhaustion, light, and darkness.

Source: Wikipedia: Cuttlefish in their home environment
originally posted to Flickr as Cuttlefish laying eggs
Author prilfish (Silke Baron)

Dr. Whitmont dives deeply into the cuttlefish's anatomy, which is part shell with soft parts, as well as its behaviors, and he relates these characteristics to human tendencies. For example, the cuttlefish sprays dark ink (the source of sepia coloring in old photographs) to confuse its predators and allow it to slink away in self-protection. Similarly, the person who needs the remedy *Sepia* may put forth a black mood in order to be left in solitude when the demands of social interaction become exhausting. Indeed, there is something absolutely mournful looking about the cuttlefish with its head burdened by eight tentacles and its sad eyes.

I visited the Monterey Aquarium in California many years ago and saw cuttlefish there. This was after studying them from a homeopathic perspective. Several amazing things struck me. First, they floated up and down in their tanks and parts of them ballooned out like little ballerina tutus. Second, they were really quite small; I had imagined them on a scale with, perhaps, a sea turtle, but they were not. And, most amazing, they had light blue eyes and seemed to make eye contact with me through the glass wall of the tank. I treasure this opportunity to make such intimate contact with a humble though dynamic mollusk.

It might at first seem far–fetched to imagine that something as inert as minerals can somehow reflect human characteristics, but they do. Dr. Whitmont provides clear analogues between gold and the human psyche. He establishes the link between gold and the sun in ancient and alchemical circles, where gold was highly valued and often revered. For the alchemists, the ability to transmute base metal into gold was a deeply spiritual pursuit, not only in metallurgy but also in the transcendence of base human nature. Because of its value, gold was typically the treasure and currency only of royalty, not the general population.

While we are not likely to see a real king in our homeopathic consulting room, we do see people who feel kingly toward their families and even their employees. Good kings were responsible for ensuring that their subjects' needs were met and that they were protected from enemies. When kings fail in these tasks and roles, they may be deeply affected emotionally. For example, a father who loses his job and cannot provide for his family may sink into a depression that can best be treated by homeopathic gold—called *Aurum*. It is important to note, and central to understanding homeopathy, that every person who fails as a provider does not become depressed. Some become angry, some abandon their families, and some redouble their efforts to earn income. But those who become depressed, even to the point of suicide, might be helped by *Aurum*.

So how do we homeopaths make the match? We are shamanistic in our ability to find the relationship between the suffering person and the substance in nature that will heal that person. I will review how this is done in the following chapters as we explore the link between the elements of Shamanism and homeopathy and journey to the nature-spirit kingdoms.

CHAPTER TWO

Core Elements of Shamanism and Homeopathy

Those who carry the pain of others hold the power to heal. It is the price of being a healer. It is an impossible role, but it must be done so that others may survive. Please pray for us and know that we are here to help the earth continue.

(Connor p. 103)

Because homeopathic medicines give no sensory clues about their origin, it is virtually impossible to understand how the nature spirit of the source is contained within them.

While the shamans of central Asia have been seen as prototypes by western researchers and explorers, shamanistic elements are found in Japanese, Hindu, Greek, Native American, and Tibetan cultures, and in virtually all early societies, including Christian mysticism. There has been a revived interest in Shamanism in the West. Schools with classrooms as well as virtual studies have become very popular.

My intention is to show the power of homeopathy, not by aligning it with or comparing it to another powerful form of healing, but to reveal how the energy of Shamanism is *implicit* within homeopathy. While it is perhaps not a perfect alignment, enough of the core elements and their characteristics are present in each system. You may be surprised to see the connection.

In later chapters I will discuss in detail how each of these core shamanic elements informs homeopathic treatment; for now I will introduce them in an overview. The following list of core elements of Shamanism is rather similar across cultures, countries, and time:

1. The Shaman
2. The Trance
3. The Journey
4. The Ancestors
5. The Patient / Client
6. Nature Spirits

Following is an overview of each of the core shamanic elements and a discussion of their relationship with homeopathy.

The Shaman

> It is who the student is—the person in whom the practice manifests—that is at least as important as what that practitioner knows. This is the 'who' upon which all of one's shamanic healing ability ultimately rests. (Steve Serr, Ph.D., Shamanism-101.com)

Shamans consider their work sacred, and many undergo an initiation in preparation for their work. Often they are selected by their tribe or inherit the title through their family. For some healers, suffering and surviving a serious illness mark a potential shaman. They may undergo years of arduous training to refine their skills and become effective. Their role is to mediate between their community and the natural world in order to access the energy of the natural world and make it available to heal the sick. They feel a kinship with all of life and may use trance to approach the spirits of nature.

Various cultures have different types of shamanic initiation. For example, the Kahunas of Hawaii have training that is vastly different from the arduous and highly ascetic practices of Japanese shamanistic training. (Kalweit pp. 20-21) Regardless of the cultural context, shamans are expected to master themselves through experiences that may include solitude and fasting while they receive instruction from worldly mentors or directly from nature and divinities particular to their society.

Similarly, homeopaths take their work and prepare for it very seriously. Homeopaths train for their profession over a course of years, and they are changed in the process. Some enter classroom training; others have online courses or combinations of both. They enter a world characterized by arcane subjects, a strange language, and unique processes. When well trained, they have the skills and tools to produce profound and lasting effects on their patients. Often their treatment affects the patient more deeply than even the patient realizes. Their goal is always to achieve the highest level of healing possible.

Homeopaths tend to be isolated in their practices and not to have familial ties with other homeopaths. We self-select rather than inherit our roles. It takes years of study to become a homeopath, and most of us continue to study and learn for our whole lives. The best training programs are three- or four-year programs, followed by supervised clinical casework. Currently there are very few homeopathic schools in the US, and this loss is keenly felt within the profession. We study our art and science, but are not revered by whole communities. Individually our patients love and appreciate us, but in a private, not public, way. We have no public persona or profile for the most part.

The Trance

Shamans are known to induce altered states of consciousness in themselves and their patients in order to facilitate their access to nature spirits. Techniques such as drumming, using smoke, and the use of hallucinogenic substances may be employed to reach altered, even ecstatic, states. It is in this state, that they are able to travel to their secret worlds and make contact with powerful forces in nature. Modern day, western-trained shamans are encouraged to alter their consciousness without the use of hallucinogenics, relying instead on chants and drumming, for example.

Homeopaths do not shake rattles or beat drums, but we are adept at inducing a state, which might be compared to a trance, to initiate a free flow of information—some of it quite personal—from the patient. We also maintain a state that is both highly alert and simultaneously relaxed. This is an alpha state, one that is conscious but differs from ordinary wakefulness. This is how the alpha state is explained on mind-your-reality.com:

> The relaxed detached awareness achieved during light meditation is characteristic of Alpha and is optimal for programming your mind for success. Alpha heightens your imagination, visualization, memory, learning and concentration. It lies at the base of your conscious awareness and is the gateway to your subconscious mind.

It is a tenet of our practice that we do not direct the patient's communication, except with occasional gentle questions. The ability to take what is communicated and use it to find the healing substance is quite an amazing skill.

I was privileged to study with master homeopaths at Hahnemann College in the San Francisco Bay Area.

Along with communicating a storm of information about remedies, they also provided formative training. This means we learned to be a homeopath—to think like one, to act like one, and to analyze information like one. This was very much like an initiation. The whole process was subtle, and I did not even know that it had happened until several years into my practice. This type of training develops a practitioner who has mastered the art of case taking and prescribing by combining a knowledge of human nature and a familiarity with remedies.

The Journey

Shamans journey to unseen worlds, typically described as the three worlds—upper, middle, and lower. Each has its function in providing information regarding the patient and a potential healing. Beings met in the worlds may include ancestors, gods, demons, and nature spirits. It is the task of the shaman to "hear" the messages received in the different worlds and interpret them for the patient.

The journey is the trip we homeopaths make to the world of nature—which is the source of remedies—to find the one that fits the patient. I know, after many years of practice, that "what I seek is seeking me." This means that in the relaxed, but highly attentive state of case-taking, I become receptive to communication from the natural world - the source of remedies. We are taught to analyze cases meticulously, using the books and software of *Repertories* (the list of symptoms by anatomical systems) and *Materia Medica* (the alphabetical list of remedies).

We also have inner maps to help us hone in on the type of remedy we might need. Experienced homeopaths who are good at their work will acknowledge that they often perceive the name or concept of a remedy or a remedy group in their awareness before they have even begun the process of analysis.

The Ancestors

Shamans are aware that illness may not be limited to the patient but may have also infected his family and ancestors. Sometimes healing must be done with these individuals as well, and the ancestors may show up during the trance to perform a healing. It is thought that, from their existence beyond death, they perceive the shadow or heaviness of the disease or habits they inflicted on their offspring and are now willing to help eradicate this burden.

I begin my consultation by obtaining a history of the patient. Unlike a clinician taking a typical medical history, I am not particularly concerned with lab tests and values, but I am very concerned with emotional and physical information and with dreams and fears. I also want to know which diseases and causes of death are prevalent in the patient's family. This can point to a place on the "map" of remedies called a miasm. A miasm is a predisposition to a certain type of disease.

Samuel Hahnemann felt that miasms are energetically transmitted from parents to children. This means that there may be no biological basis for this inherited tendency, but an energetic one that is transferred during conception, pregnancy, and birth, and sometimes in the environment of the home. It is not known precisely how this happens, but we do know that family members tend to have similar diseases that can be associated with certain miasms.

Hahnemann recognized three miasms, and in the 200 years since his work we have added seven more, and some of these additions are refinements of those he described. The ten miasms now recognized in homeopathy are explained comprehensively in *Miasms of the New Millennium* by Roger Morrison and Nancy Herrick. The chapter on Ancestors describe miasms and their critical role in helping patients regain their health. By acknowledging and understanding them, we are able to contact the influence of the ancestors. Although miasms present an obstacle to a complete cure, when they are eradicated in the patient, they can stop further transmission of the miasmatic energy and can heal, not only the patient, but the whole lineage going forward in time.

The Patient

It goes without saying that each shamanic or homeopathic encounter requires a patient. The patient is the person who is sick, usually on many levels, and who has asked for help. The patient usually asks for healing only of the symptoms they find most bothersome. They do not realize that their allergies may have originated following a period of unresolved grief or that their indigestion developed after betrayal by a lover.

It is the work of the homeopath to delve into the origin and timing of disease in order to effect a complete cure.

Shamans as well as homeopaths also recognize that disease runs through the entire person—the mental, emotional, spiritual and physical bodies. They know that physical healing alone will not produce a permanent cure. Whether healed by a shaman or a homeopath, patients must cooperate with their healing—sometimes by avoiding certain foods or activities, sometimes by enduring the return of old symptoms or the temporary worsening of current ones. These developments speak to the power, and, if you will, the sanctity of the intervention or healing force.

Nature Spirit Power

Most people are familiar with the fact that shamans seek healing power in nature to match the vibration of the person or his illness. Power animals and healing plants are invited to contribute their energies to cure the sick person. Because homeopathic medicines give no sensory clues about their origin, it is virtually impossible to understand how the nature spirit of the source is contained within them. This fact alone has made it difficult for people to appreciate the power of homeopathy. How does the homeopath access the spirits in nature? How can spirits of substances such as snake poison, sea water, or hawthorn (to give a few examples) or any other animal, plant, or mineral be contained within the pills?

The power of natural substances is contained within remedies as a result of their very systematic and thorough preparation. Even before a remedy is prepared and made available, an arduous process called "proving" must be completed in order to determine which illnesses it will cure. Remedy preparation and proving will be explained in the next chapter. Most people who learn about these processes for the first time are amazed and have an "aha" moment as they begin to perceive and appreciate the power of homeopathic remedies.

CHAPTER THREE

Genie in a Bottle

To see a World in a Grain of Sand

And a Heaven in a Wild Flower,

Hold Infinity in the palm of your hand

And Eternity in an hour.

William Blake

What the eyes perceive in herbs or stones or trees is not yet a remedy; the eyes see only the dross.

Paracelsus

What does a genie in a bottle mean? There are many interpretations, but at the core it means that something very powerful is housed in a small container. I chose this analogy because it speaks to the scientific magic required to create a homeopathic remedy. It also speaks to the ethereal nature of the substance that remains in the remedy.

You may be wondering how a powerful form of healing like Shamanism can have anything in common with the innocuous-looking little white sugar pills you know as homeopathic medicine. The truth is, those pills pack a mighty punch that compresses, encodes, and delivers the healing force of whichever animal, plant, or mineral is their source. Despite the fact that all homeopathic remedies in pill-form look, taste, and smell the same, they are vastly different in their origin and their effect.

If you take a trip to a health food store that carries the "blue-tube" display of homeopathic remedies made by Boiron, you may find *Lachesis*, for example. *Lachesis* is made from the venom of the bushmaster snake, and the venom is a very poisonous substance. *Chamomilla*, which will be in the same display, is, on the other hand, a remedy made from the humble and mild chamomile flower. Far from being lethal or mighty, the chamomile flower is a small, almost timid plant that is known to be non-toxic and soothing. If you examine the pills inside the vials of these two remedies, you will see that they are indistinguishable, though one is made from venom and the other from a shy flower.

How Homeopathic Remedies are made

I will now explain, step by step, how the genie is captured—that is how a powerful source in nature can be contained within little pills. While I will take you through the five-step process required to make a remedy in pill-form, it is worth remarking that some homeopathic products are in liquid form and some are topical creams. There are even some new products that are sprays. The process for making these is somewhat different, but the result is the same—the original substance has been converted to an energetic form.

Another important fact to emphasize is the all homeopathic laboratories in this country are FDA-approved and regulated. Equivalent governing bodies oversee the processes in laboratories in other countries as well. This ensures both sterility, safety, and consistency in the products. Despite the cost to the laboratory to comply with government regulations, remedies are very inexpensive to purchase, and one vial provides many doses.

The five steps for making a remedy are first, procuring the source material; second, preparing the source material to change it into a substance that can be diluted; third, adding water to dilute the material; fourth, forcefully shaking the remedy between dilutions; and, fifth, medicating sucrose/lactose or other types of pellets to absorb the resulting liquid remedy. These processes are employed in homeopathic laboratories around the world using nearly identical techniques. It is worth taking time to acquaint you with these processes so that you can begin to understand what the "simple white pills" *really* are. We will follow the preparation of the remedy *Apis mellifica* from the honey bee to illustrate the process.

1. Procuring the source material

The source material for homeopathic remedies can be either liquid or solid. It can be something from the animal, mineral, or plant kingdoms. Animal sources vary from the female's milk traditionally used for mammals, to feathers of birds, to whole insects. Plant sources can be leaves, stems, flowers, bark, or roots, or a combination of these. If the source is solid, such as mineral or plant sources, a small amount of the material is ground with a dissolving substance. This process, called trituration, produces a mixture that can then be prepared as a liquid. If the source material is liquid or can be dissolved in liquid, then a "mother" tincture, or source tincture, is produced from this, as we will show with the example of the bee.

2. Converting the source material to a tincture

The raw source from nature—in this example a honey bee—must be converted to a form that can be diluted. To accomplish this, one bee would be soaked in alcohol for a prescribed amount of time until it is essentially dissolved. The resulting liquid of the source material is called the mother tincture and forms the basis for making the remedy. It is worth noting that living creatures only rarely need to be sacrificed to make a remedy, since other parts can usually be used. If an insect is sacrificed, it makes enough remedy to yield millions of vials; so one bee goes a very long way!

Rules for converting the source material to a tincture are contained in the *Homeopathic Pharmacopeia of the United States* (HPUS) and are very precise. This is not kitchen-sink or intuitive work. This is a science that produces uniform medicines around the world.

3. Diluting the resulting substance

The power of dilution is a very difficult concept for people to accept. Usually we think that by diluting liquids we are weakening the substance. Just the opposite is true in homeopathy, as will be discussed in the section describing nanoparticles.

There are various formulas for dilution, but I will discuss one that is commonly used. Take one drop of bee mother tincture and add 99 drops of sterile water. Shake it up (see next step). Then, take one drop of this mixture and add 99 drops of sterile water. When you have done this six times, you have made a remedy at the 6C potency. "C" stands for 100 in Roman numerals, and this is the number of drops of water used in each dilution. Six is the number of times you have diluted it. Believe it or not, this is considered a low potency (strength) remedy. This also produces a level of dilution where there is virtually no molecule of the original substance remaining in the liquid. Remedies in the 6C potency are readily available in health food stores, as are those in the 30C potency which repeats the process 30 times.

4. Succussion or forceful pounding of the diluted substance to fully develop its potential

This fourth step is done between each dilution, and it fully develops the remedy. The liquid must be shaken vigorously. If one is making a remedy by hand, the container of the original substance and water may be banged against a firm, resilient surface such as book or table top, at least 12 times for each dilution. Some laboratories, however, use a gentler succussion method. Fortunately, there are machines that accomplish the dilution and succussion processes, and hands can be saved from this trauma!

Another difficult concept to understand is that the more times the material has been diluted *and* shaken, the stronger it is. Strength in remedies is called potency; and potency increases with dilution and shaking. The reason for this is due to the creation of more and more nanoparticles (explained below). Because high potencies act very strongly on the mind and emotions, they are usually not available in retail stores, whose products are aimed at first-aid and self-care treatment.

5. Pellet medication

After dissolving the source material and then diluting and shaking-up the liquid, the resulting liquid is added to a container of sucrose or sucrose/lactose pellets until the pellets are saturated. They are then dried in a very controlled, specified way, to avoid cross-contamination with other remedies. These pills are then put into glass or plastic vials and labeled. In this example the vials would be labelled *Apis mellifica* (honey bee) 6C, or 30C, or 200C, or whatever potency has been prepared. All the tinctures look pretty much alike, and the pills retain their white color even after being saturated with the liquid.

It is worth emphasizing that this work is done not only with care, and compliance with regulations, but with reverence. The pharmacists and lab workers acknowledge the sanctity of their work—harnessing nature for healing. One major laboratory was known to begin each work day with a prayer circle for their employees.

Obviously, extreme care must be taken to label remedies correctly. Care is also taken to comply with FDA guidelines regarding sterility and accuracy of the product. One major manufacturer of homeopathic remedies carries *Apis* in 6C, 9C, 12C, 15C, 18C, 21C, 24C, 30C, 100C, 200C, and 500C potencies, along with even higher strengths.

This may give you some idea of how diligent the manufacturer must be, as well as the subtlety homeopaths use in prescribing remedies since some of the potencies are close to each other. It is worth mentioning that remedies, when well-cared for, (kept from heat, direct current, and strong odors) will be active indefinitely. They really do not expire, despite the FDA's insistence that expiration dates be added to each vial.

Nanoparticles and the Memory of Water

When I studied homeopathy over 20 years ago, our instructors said, "We know that homeopathy works, but we

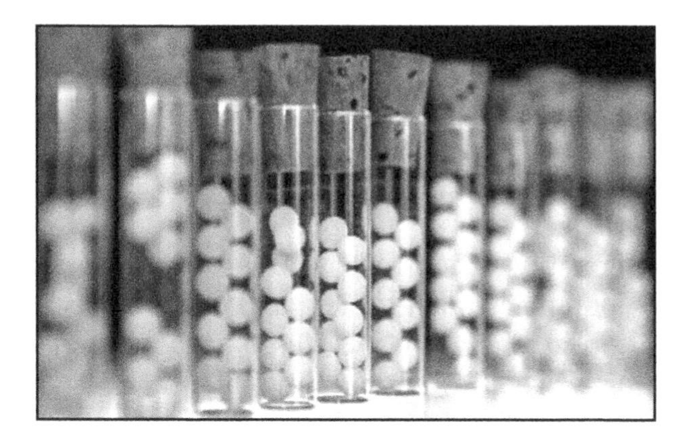

don't know how." All that has changed; but don't be surprised if you did not see it in news headlines! It is now recognized that the power of the remedy is due to the nanoparticles that are created during the dilution and succussion process. A nanoparticle is a particle so small that it is invisible to the naked eye. Nanoparticles function differently from larger molecules and have increasing applications in science, manufacturing, and—guess what —conventional medicine. For example, they are used in medicine for precise delivery of medications to certain cells.

How do we get to nanoparticles from the mother tincture? By diluting the source material (for example the dissolved bee) over and over until there is virtually nothing left of it in a molecular sense. However, the energetic imprint of the source (the bee) is in the water. Below is a reprint of the abstract of the seminal article that explains this. It summarizes research done on the homeopathic preparations of remedies from a metallic source in the 30C and 200C potency to determine whether any source material remained. As you will read, it does remain. It is worthwhile to reflect that this "proof" was made over 200 years after Samuel Hahnemann predicted that the power of the remedy is stronger when it is more dilute. I am sure he did not have such powerful equipment at hand, either.

> Homeopathy is controversial because medicines in high potencies such as 30c and 200c involve huge dilution factors (1060 and 10400, respectively) which are many orders of magnitude greater than Avogadro's number, so that theoretically there should be no measurable remnants of the starting materials. No hypothesis which predicts the retention of properties of starting materials has been proposed nor has any physical entity been shown to exist in these high potency medicines. Using market samples of metal derived medicines from reputable manufacturers, we have demonstrated for the first time by Transmission Electron Microscopy (TEM), electron diffraction and chemical analysis by Inductively Coupled Plasma-Atomic Emission Spectroscopy (ICP-AES), *the presence of physical entities in these extreme dilutions, in the form of nanoparticles of the starting metals and their aggregates.* [Emphasis added] *Homeopathy (2010)* 99, 231-242)

Jacques Benveniste, a French immunologist, published a paper in *Nature* in 1988 that caused a storm within scientific circles, leading to the collapse of Benveniste's career, and, some say, his demise. The paper reported:

> that white blood cells called basophils, which control the body's reaction to allergens, can be activated to produce an immune response by solutions of antibodies that have been diluted so far that they contain none of these biomolecules at all. It was as though the water molecules somehow retained a memory of the antibodies that they had previously been in contact with, so that a biological effect remained when the antibodies were no longer present. This, it seemed, validated the claims made for highly diluted homeopathic medicines. (nature.com/news/2004/041004/full/news041004-19.html)

The work was later reproduced by Nobel Prize winner, Luc Montagnier and an Italian colleague with the same findings. Even with such credentials behind the proof of the memory of water, the scientific community still considers this research fringe and unimportant.

How a Remedy is used

Now that we have made it, what can the remedy *Apis* accomplish? Like most remedies, *Apis* affects many organs and systems of the body. One of the first-aid uses of *Apis* is to relieve the pain of a bee or insect sting. This happens when it is taken orally, in fairly low potency (6C or 12C). Why low potency? Because a bee sting is not a systemic or serious event. However, if a person is allergic to bee stings, a sting can be a life-threatening event. In that case, *Apis* should be taken in at least a 30C potency, and an Epipen, a preloaded vial of epinephrine, should be ready in case it is needed to address anaphylactic shock. It is my experience, however, that repeated use of *Apis* following bee stings can actually desensitize a person to bee stings and prevent future shock episodes. *Apis* remedies can also be used for sore throats, certain types of urinary tract infections, and a host of other issues. It almost seems that William Blake was thinking of this when he wrote the poem reproduced at the beginning of the chapter.

Discovering Remedies

How do homeopaths discover what conditions a remedy can cure? We follow the same principles that Samuel Hahnemann articulated when he first came upon the idea of giving dilute doses of a substance to healthy people in order to determine which symptoms would appear in the person. This form of research is called conducting "provings" and is carried out today in much the same way Hahnemann did it. Hahnemann actually proved over 90 remedies during his lifetime! Once you have read how painstaking the process is, you too will be amazed at his diligence. Remember, he did this while supporting a large family, translating medical texts, fleeing or rebuffing critics within established medicine, and maintaining a homeopathic practice.

The principle involved in proving a remedy is that a natural substance, when diluted and succussed and taken by a healthy person, will bring on the symptoms of the disease that the substance is likely to cure. Since the person is basically healthy, the symptoms will be rather minor, although noticeable, and transient.

Provings are conducted on groups of about 10-30 people. The subjects never know what substance in being tested. Many times even the "proving master," the person conducting the trial, does not know what substance is being tested. This is very similar to the double-blind format used in conventional medical research. The subjects take one dose of the remedy, usually in a 30C potency, and then keep a meticulous journal of all the mental, emotional, and physical changes that occur to them during the next month. No change is too small to record. As you can imagine, this produces a ream of material. How is it sorted?

During a "proving meeting," each subject reports on his or her experiences. It is amazing to see the concurrence of major symptoms and themes that reveal themselves. These are then systematized and categorized by the organs and systems of the body, and accepted as symptoms that the remedy will cure.

For example, in the area of headache, many provers may have developed a headache in their right temple shortly after eating. If they did not have this symptom previously, it is taken to be an indication of the type of headache that will be cured by the remedy being tested. Mood changes are of equal importance. For example, experiences of irritability or impatience after taking the remedy will mean that the remedy can alleviate irritability and impatience, when it is the specific type the provers reported.

As you may have concluded, this is a painstaking and subtle process. My brief description provides just a glimpse into the care and detail required for proving new remedies. The entire profession, as well as homeopathic patients worldwide, is indebted to the homeopaths who undertake this arduous work.

Now that we know how nature is captured inside the small white pills, in the next chapter I will discuss the selection, training, and work of both homeopaths and shamans. It is apparent that the tools of Shamanism—dress, rattles, drums, hallucinogenic substances, smoke, and other artifacts that convey power, are often used during the Shamanic healing. For the homeopath, the little white pills are their only physical tool, but a lot of work has gone into their preparation.

CHAPTER FOUR

Homeopaths and Shamans

You have to move slowly and carefully in order
to cross the distance. You have to contain – to
remember. You must construct an inner map for
without it you will be lost. You must realize your eyes
have ambushed you. You have never seen anything.
With conjure eyes, you can see once more.
You can see our desperate condition.

(Carson, p. 20)

Homeopaths

Name a famous homeopath. There must be some, right? Don't be concerned if you cannot name even one. Most people have no idea who the homeopathic lights in this world are unless they are homeopaths themselves. There were many famous homeopaths in the past, and there are quite a few in the leadership of the profession right now. Some are American, and many are Indian and British; a few are Italians; and at least one Greek homeopath comes to mind. Homeopaths rarely step outside the confines of their profession to achieve recognition. Fame, if it can be called that, comes from teaching, publishing, conducting provings (homeopathic research), and, less often, being well known as a skilled clinician. Why are skilled clinicians not recognized more widely? Their reputation is usually geographically limited to the client base they serve.

Occasionally, a homeopath moves in more visible circles, such as inside the British Royal family. This was the case with Peter Fisher, MD, whose untimely and accidental death the homeopathic world mourned. Dr. Fisher was homeopathic consultant to the royal family in Britain. Yes, they use homeopathy, but they do not speak openly about this, despite the fact that it probably accounts for their robust health and longevity. Following is an excerpt from the *London Telegraph's* article about Dr. Fisher's death, dated August 16, 2018:

Greg white, chief executive of the Faculty of Homeopathy, said: 'We have lost a leader, not just for the faculty but for homeopathy in the UK and worldwide. It's no exaggeration to say Peter is an irreplaceable talent. He truly was a giant in all his fields of endeavour, which included clinician, research and academic.

A sometimes controversial figure, Dr. Fisher believed passionately in the power of homeopathy, a belief that highly diluted substances can induce the body to heal itself. The practice is regarded as no better than a placebo by most of the medical profession and has now been all but banished from the NHS. His advocacy alongside his position in the royal household attracted some criticism, but he always pointed out that homeopathists [sic] have been treating the Royal Family since the reign of Queen Victoria.

However, he revealed in an interview with The Daily Telegraph in January that, three years after taking up his position in 2001, he received a 'serious dressing down' from the head of the medical household, Sir Richard Thompson, for mentioning his Royal connection during a public argument about homeopathy.

Most homeopaths can relate to the mixed message Dr. Fisher received: "Do your best work, but keep a low profile." We are a hidden, even a persecuted profession. Homeopathy, in and of itself, is not a licensed profession, although some homeopaths are licensed in other fields. It relies on certification to designate those who have achieved a certain level of competence in the field. Anyone can claim to be a homeopath since it has no baseline training requirements. This rather loose system creates a lot of confusion within the profession, not to say mixed results with patients.

Homeopathy has long been disparaged by organized medicine, which has referred to the "little pills" as either poison or placebo. In 2017, the FDA launched a full-scale attack on the safety of homeopathy despite negligible reports of any injury being attributed to homeopathic treatment over a period of decades. The agency's final regulations are still pending at this time. So the profession operates in the shadows, is not well understood, has no leadership in the world, and, finally, is open to persecution and ridicule. That is the morphogenetic field that a new homeopath enters when they begin practicing; and it envelops us all our professional days. This is the inheritance from our professional predecessors that we share with our contemporaries. It bears a strong resemblance to what Samuel Hahnemann experienced all through his life. Many of us jokingly refer to it as the homeopathic miasm.

A Hidden Profession

Homeopaths tend to be rather scholarly and remain in the background of the healing world. They are poor participants in multi-disciplinary professional teams, not because they disdain other modalities, but because their treatment is more successful when used as a solo approach. If, for example, a patient takes a homeopathic remedy and simultaneously changes her diet, and/or begins taking supplements, it can be difficult to determine the action of the remedy. Knowing the effect of the remedy is key to ensuring success in prescribing.

We also individualize our treatment to each patient. We do not, for example, have remedies to treat specific diseases; rather, we treat the *person* with the disease. Six patients with the same symptoms may each receive a different remedy. We are also less interested in diagnosis or in disease names, but highly interested in symptoms and how the situation is affecting the patient. We are always looking at the big picture—how and when the illness began, what other symptoms are associated with it, and what the family tendency to disease is. We do indeed treat the whole person. If this sounds complicated and difficult, I can assure you that it is.

It seems that exercising political will and savvy are inimical to the homeopathic temperament. The profession is politically disorganized with no apparent intention of organizing itself. Homeopathy flourished briefly after Hahnemann's death in 1843. In 1910, it was soundly attacked and ultimately suppressed in this country by the US government as a result of the Flexner Report. This nationwide survey of medical school curricula had an underlying political agenda. Two thirds of the schools at that time were homeopathic or naturopathic, and the report found them wanting in teaching the biomedical model that the newly organized American Medical Association wished to promote. This report effectively put homeopathic schools and practitioners out of business in favor of allopathic (conventional) medical schools, organized medicine, and pharmaceutical treatment. Homeopathy and Naturopathy were declared unscientific when compared to allopathic methods.

Homeopathy then went underground in the US until the 70s, when it emerged as part of the rights movements of the time—Civil Rights, Women's Rights, Gay Rights, etc.—and ultimately developed a high degree of professionalism and training programs. In other countries, homeopathy was spared such political attacks; it is more accepted in France, Germany, Italy, some parts of South America, and India.

Homeopathic Initiation and Lineage

My own journey into homeopathy began with a complete cure of a serious illness, but this is not everyone's story. I have told this story in detail in the Preface to this book. It was not until several years after experiencing this miracle that I decided to pursue the study of homeopathy in a professional training program. Between the time of my recovery and undertaking the formal study of homeopathy, I learned more about it on my own and began to use it for myself and my family. I believe I had a homeopathic initiation through my illness. Without this inciting event, homeopathy might just have passed me by entirely.

Shamans

> ...the term shaman has been widely adopted by anthropologists to refer to specific groups of healers in diverse cultures who have sometime been called

> medicine men, witch doctors, sorcerers, wizards, magicians or seers. ...shamans can voluntarily enter altered states of consciousness, and in these states they experience themselves journeying to other realms. (Walsh pp. 8, 10)

Shamans use these journeys to acquire knowledge or power that is used to heal individuals or their community. The natural world they contact is the same world that homeopaths use to find and source their remedies, although the two methods of contact are quite different.

Shamans and Initiation

In some cultures, shamans are identified when they develop the "shaman's sickness"—often a near-death experience which, upon their recovery, marks them as able to navigate the worlds of life and death and access the power of nature to heal.

> The shamans of pre-Soviet Tuva were healers, diviners, and conductors of rituals necessary for Tuvan life. Both men and women became shamans after they were visited with the 'shaman's sickness.' Often, a shaman interpreted this as invasion by the spirit of a dead shaman. This invading Being wanted the living person to become a shaman. The onset of this illness was commonly early in life, but also occurred in people more than 40 years of age. If the person ignored the calling, continued sickness or even death occurred. The illness frequently manifested itself as fainting spells, memory loss, or convulsions. Heeding

> the call resulted in a complete remission of symptoms. (Foundation for Shamanic Studies, *Tuva, Land of Eagles—The Foundation's 1993 Expedition to Tuva*, Bill Brunton © Shamanism, Spring 1994, Vol. 7, No. 1)

Sometimes shamans are biological members of a shamanic family or the offspring of a shaman. There is power in the lineage, and it is considered necessary to observe rather strict rules in the care and raising of a child who is destined to be a shaman. This is a burden on the family as well as on the growing child, whose natural childhood and attendant freedoms are often restricted as he is prepared for his future role.

Whether marked by illness or selected through lineage, shamans have a high profile within their group. Once they have undergone their initiation and training and proved their ability to heal, shamans are revered, perhaps even feared, by their community. It is understood that they can communicate with unseen forces, and that they may hold the key to life and death for an individual. This high profile is quite the opposite for homeopaths. Though they also harness the power of nature for healing, they are often unacknowledged.

How Shamans are Perceived

Many western shamans, much like homeopaths, now self-select, and undertake training programs that, while maintaining the essence of shamanic traditions, are geared to modern students. Such students may want to use the healing techniques of shamanism for themselves and their friends only, or they may want to become recognized within a larger community.

Similar to homeopathy, there is no minimum requirement of study or apprenticeship to become a shaman, and there is no credentialing. Yet, as a group, shamans seem to stir interest and command respect from the general public. Since working with a shaman is considered offbeat and far outside the norm of western forms of healing, Shamanism, while more marginalized than homeopathy, is also more politically protected. It seems to be able to raise its feathered head and beat its drums loudly and the FDA continues to look the other way. Both forms of healing use methods that are hard to understand, but easy to accept when they are successful.

The words of Mary, a Native American conjure (shaman or healer), spoken to her would-be student, seem applicable to both shamans and homeopaths:

> The conjure walks a trail of loneliness. It is a road that few others will follow, a solitary occupation. Yet you will see things no other human will see. The night will have day eyes and the day will have night eyes. Believe me you will walk through hardscrabble and thorny places. It's a long and difficult trail, but only then will your heart open to all that is. Yes, you must go into the beating heart of the world. By doing that you will go deep into your own heart. In that understanding is your birth as a conjure. (Carson p. 20)

Whether formed or found, chosen or self-selected, both shamans and homeopaths undertake the huge tasks of attempting to relieve people of their burdens at many levels. And both professions must accept their limitations even as they rejoice at their victories and their patients being restored to health. In the next chapters we will examine the techniques that each practitioner uses and how they use them.

CHAPTER FIVE

The Trance

Altered States of consciousness belong to the natural history of mankind; they should be seen in the framework of human sensory activity and have little to do with religion and faith. They are physical phenomena, a matter of biology. They are partially chemical and partially energetic processes.

(Kalweit p. 82)

Take a journey to a hidden world—what an invitation! We can all respond to this— some of us choosing to take an outer journey to remote places, like the Amazon; some wanting to reach other planets as soon as the technology can support the journey; and some of us traveling inward, to the vast time/space matrix of consciousness. This is what shamans do.

To ensure the success of their journey, shamans alter their consciousness to align it with the forces they wish to contact. Their goal is to "converse" with plants, animals, and rocks in order to open a dialogue in a shared language. Consciousness-altering methods have been available for as long as there have been humans. Some of the simpler yet profound methods include meditation, contemplation, drumming, and chanting. Brainwave measurements of meditators, drummers, and chanters reveal that they are in altered states. Drugs can also alter consciousness; we know about the "high" that marijuana can produce, and we may have experienced it. It is also possible that we have experienced an altered reality directly without the aid of any substance.

Substances are not necessary to produce an altered state, where oneness with all nature, including people, is experienced. The Dali Lama, for example, seems to be in a perpetually altered state. He laughs heartily, speaks without inhibition, and loves unconditionally. Few of us can maintain such a state for any length of time; yet we intuitively know that it is a balm to our own souls as well as for others. We can trust that the Dali Lama does not use any particular substance to access his peace and bliss. Rather, it seems to have become a permanent state, a trait that results from years of meditation and inner work.

In this chapter I will discuss trance and the way it operates for both shamans and homeopaths. Trance states are a given for shamans and can sometimes be dramatic; they are a necessary component of their work. A colleague has advised me, however, that not all homeopaths will agree with, or be comfortable with, the idea that a trance state has anything to do with homeopathic work. I can understand that, so I will refer to the state we homeopaths enter to do our work as an altered or intuitive state of consciousness.

Shamanism and Trance

> The shamanic state of consciousness—referred to as ecstasy, trance, etc.—is a form of consciousness practiced and developed to reach another, shamanic reality. All of this is done in order to do such things as find answers to questions from spirit teachers, gain assistance in solving problems, find a way back to wellness and health, or regain a natural empowerment with the assistance of power animals. (*Natural Trance and Ecstasy: The Shamanic Journey to Drum and Rattle*, Steve Serr, PhD, shamanism-101.com)

Is the trance state difficult to access? Michael Pollan entered a trance state when he took hallucinogenic drugs and experienced the leaves and flowers returning his gaze (as related in Chapter One). Many people probably have had a similar experience, while others may want this but are not sure how to access it. There is an understanding within many cultures and religions that somewhere along the way we have lost our innocence and have become hardened to just these types of states. Skepticism may play a part in our closing down, as does a lack of training and ability, as well as a highly reductionist world view. This view is the dominant paradigm, and we begin to subscribe to it from infancy, although oneness is a much more relaxing state than separation. Kalweit says, "Today, unfortunately, there is a tendency to either mythologize altered states of consciousness or to discredit them." (p. 82)

Meditators, mystics, those who pray, and high-performance athletes can reach altered states, where the bodily senses are either muted or heightened, and where they can find capacities and abilities far beyond the normal day-to-day functions. "Through these altered states of consciousness, peak performances come about, extraordinary acts of strength, speed, balance, and—something that all the spectators can see—effortlessness of achievement. "{Kalweit p. 86)

The Foundation for Shamanic Studies trains western people, including an impressive number of doctors and health professionals, to become shamans. They provide instruction, a reinforcing environment, group support, and the expectation that the trance state can be reached. Testimonies from their students reveal that while not everyone succeeds the first time, most students can enter trance and journey with minimal instruction. Susan Mokelke, JD, one of the leaders at the foundation, comments below on why she believes it is easy to access the trance state:

> It has been our experience in the Foundation that the shamanic state of consciousness is part of our biological and spiritual design; thus, the widespread ability of people to successfully journey and access these hidden worlds after even one weekend. (*Core Shamanism and Daily Life*, Susan Mokelke, J.D.)

Michael Harner argues persuasively for not only the existence of non-ordinary states of consciousness but for their universality within all humans. He writes, "Recent advances in neurochemistry show that the human brain carries its own consciousness-altering drugs, including hallucinogens...." (p. xxi). Harner further elaborates on trance by stating that shamans usually work in the dark, or cover their eyes, in order to access their own light and to "focus on the aspects of non-ordinary reality essential to (their) work." (p. 22)

Shamans induce trance states with drums, rattles, chanting, and sometimes drugs. All induction techniques are directed towards establishing a more open, relaxed state in both the patient and the shaman to allow connection with realities that are beyond ordinary waking consciousness. "...if a drum rhythm is synchronized with brain wave frequencies, it is easier to achieve an altered state of consciousness. To this must be added the courage to let oneself go completely." (Kalweit p.78)

The creation and maintenance of safe, even sacred, space is part of the shaman's ritual and undoubtedly contributes to her success. Sick people are usually anxious and may be reluctant to relinquish control. Sacred space, where powerful objects and energy can be seen and sensed, begins the process of healing through relaxation. Warmth and color and comfort are also part of it; not only for the shamans, but for most homeopaths, too. Our offices say: "Others have been able to leave their burdens here. Perhaps you will too."

> Shamans always begin healing ceremonies by opening sacred space. In this space we leave behind the affairs of ordinary life, the bustling world of meetings and schedules, and prepare to meet the divine. Sacred space allows us to enter our quiet inner world where healing takes place. (Villoldo p. 136)

> Shamanism can be seen as a fundamentally spiritual approach to real-life problem solving informed by an animistic philosophy that is practiced by individuals for the benefit of their group(s). These individuals systematically utilize a technique or combination of techniques to alter consciousness in such a way that they reliably access non ordinary reality. This reality...is the abode of conscious beings with whom these individuals (shamans) interact. Interaction with these "spirits" is a defining attribute of shamanic practice. (*The Reawakening of Shamanism in the West*, Bill Brunton, Foundation for Shamanic Studies)

"Trance" in Homeopathy

In order to explain how the trance idea operates within homeopathy, I must describe how a consultation with a patient is structured within the framework of treatment. What I will be describing is based on the practice of classical homeopathy—a form and process modeled on the method designed by Hahnemann and refined by his students and followers over time. This is how it works with me.

A potential patient contacts me by phone. I have a rather brief conversation with them to determine what type of help they need. They may say something like, "I am peri-menopausal and cannot sleep at night." Or, "I never had allergies before this year, but they are extreme and I have no energy at all." These are two conditions within my realm of competence, so I begin a bit of fact finding to determine how long they have had these problems; what they have used in order to remediate them; their overall health status; and whether they are taking any prescription or over-the-counter medication for this condition or any other. I then review the process for seeing me, and talk about my fees. If all is a go, I send them my ten-page intake form. This form asks a lot of questions that help me understand the person better.

One of the most important questions on the form is, "Has anything ever happened to you from which you never recovered?" Here I can get a lot of information about abuse, head injuries, abandonment, car accidents, and other traumas that can play a role in the development of physical symptoms. Most potential patients have no idea how important these episodes in life can be, and that my treating them so deeply may cause these traumas to resolve. They usually want a "pill for their ill," albeit, a little sugar one. But we homeopaths know that shock, grief, and abuse are mighty causative factors in producing disease. They will be glad to see, for example, that when the allergy is handled, they are much less focused on their anger over being fired—which may have brought on the allergies in the first place. It is my belief that illness does not just arise from nothing, but grows on the fertile, usually unconscious ground of our experience.

> A patient consulted me for help with her arthritis. In response to the "Did anything happen to you" question, she wrote of the shock she had several years ago when her brother, who was so much younger than she, died suddenly. She told me that not a day went by that she did not re-live this event. Her arthritis had begun at the same time! I found one remedy to help with both the arthritis and the shock. When she returned for a follow-up consultation, her arthritis was much improved. I asked if she still thought about her brother's death as often. "You know," she said, "I hardly think about that at all anymore."

My first appointment with a patient is usually two hours in length. Many patients will express surprise about the length of time needed. From experience, however, I know that they will not mind spending the time once we begin interacting. To allay their anxiety, however, I usually say that we should allow for two hours, but we can end sooner if we are finished.

Finally, the patient arrives. After the initial pleasantries are over, we enter into what I call the healing dance or, in fact, a form of light trance. My questions are open-ended, and I am truly not shocked by anything the patient says. I have never had a patient who did not enjoy their meeting with me. They love to talk about themselves and to be heard with so much attention and compassion. They enjoy my drawing parallels from different parts of their life or experience, and this often prompts them to open further. When I finally look at my watch and announce that we have been talking for two hours (often more), they are always surprised! This is because they have been in a sort of trance, where the normal sense of time passing is suspended, and they floated effortlessly from describing their symptoms to talking about their childhood, to relating dreams and fears. I require nothing of them but to keep the information flowing.

What about my trance? It took me many years to understand that I am in an alpha state during my patient interviews. The alpha state is a light hypnotic state, a relaxed yet focused and receptive way of perceiving. Beta is our ordinary waking state; delta is our sleep state, and alpha is something in between. This state makes me both highly alert and very receptive to receiving information from my spirit that will help me find the right remedy. I believe we all have spirit guides, and that they assist us with our healing work. The more we open to them, the easier life becomes.

I have two tasks to accomplish during the homeopathic consultation. One is to open widely and intuitively to receive the person before me with all their history, pain, misery, humor, egotism, bombastic style, paranoia, political intrigue, critical nature, fear, weepiness, self-pity, anxiety, or whatever state or mood they bring forth. I allow it to flow and permeate the consulting room.

My other task is to begin to understand this person within the framework of homeopathic remedy mapping. In other words, what type of person sits before me, and what type of remedy might work for them? This is a much more linear state where I am in contact with information, categories, and descriptions of remedies, and remedy families. I can literally sense my brain operate in two completely different ways at once. Neither state interferes with the other. It is as though two world views are operating together—one of the intuitive and one of the scientist. This state or trance is unique to my case-taking with a patient. It does not occur in any other time or space or situation in my life. It is as though I am simultaneously expressing both the art and science of homeopathy.

I believe that even light trance opens the inner doors so that we can allow the nature spirit to contact us. As the interview progresses, I may think of more than one nature spirit or remedy in succession, and either dismiss them or explore them further. I may get a picture, a word, or recall a typical symptom of a remedy that will lead me to the correct prescription. Sometimes I consult my *Materia Medica* (alphabetical list of remedies), or Repertories (list of symptoms organized by bodily systems). But this usually happens when the trance time is over, and the patient goes to the bathroom, gets up to stretch or gets water. We signal, by these actions, that we are re-entering ordinary reality, linear time and space again.

It is important to maintain perspective on the trance state. It is only a vehicle that allows the journey to occur. In the following chapters we will explore where shamans and homeopaths journey to contact the healing forces of nature, beginning with the power animals.

CHAPTER SIX

The Journey to the Animal Kingdom

While the mythical paradise of animal-human unity
is lost in ordinary reality, it still remains accessible
in non-ordinary reality to the shaman
and the vision seeker.

(Harner pp. 57-58)

Each of these provings is a window
into the inner life of the animal.

(Roger Morrison, Foreword to Herrick: Animal Minds, Human Voices p. x)

The journey of the shaman or the homeopath is the most private, hidden, subtle, yet powerful part of the healing experience. Where does the shaman go? It is said that she travels to the spirit world. Where is that? Can spirits actually be called to the space of the shaman and patient? I believe they can. It is well known that shamans contact animals to become their own protector and to heal their patients.

Homeopaths also use animal power in their healing, though this is less known and understood. Using some comparisons between the animals sought, we can find a surprising amount of congruence between the two journeys. Villoldo (pp. 140-146) identifies four main power animals sought for their healing qualities; I will discuss three of them and indicate their relationship to homeopathic remedies made from the same source.

The first is the serpent, which he describes as "the most universal archetype, representing a primeval connection to the feminine, to fertility, and sexuality." This is similar to how the snakes used in homeopathic remedies are characterized. His second power animal is the jaguar, which represents "sudden transformation and death." The homeopathic remedy made from Black Jaguar suits a person who is loud, overbearing, and given to rage and anger; this person is also preoccupied with justice. The third one is the eagle, which brings vision, clarity, foresight, and self-transcendence. Homeopathically, the eagle patient feels he has the power to move between parallel worlds—one of reality and one of spirit. These characterizations are abbreviated examples of the qualities attributed to shamanic power animals or animals made into homeopathic remedies.

Where does the homeopath go to obtain the healing power of nature for the patient? The homeopath cannot embark on a wandering journey, taking years, like Odysseus, to return home. Nor does she travel to the various worlds of the shaman. The time limit of two hours for a consultation may or may not be sufficient to achieve the proper connection of the patient to their healing substance. So what maps are in place to inform this journey? We have already mentioned the ancestors, or miasms, and will discuss that map at greater length in Chapter Nine. There is another map used by the homeopath—and that is the map of the kingdoms.

Each of the major kingdoms—animal, plant, and mineral—has its own set of characteristics, and these are already present in the patient who reveals them through their behavior, dress, speech, history, interests, fears, dreams and the many aspects we homeopaths use to understand our patients. Then there are subcategories within the three kingdoms that further help us refine our search. For now, we will journey with the (homeopathic) animals.

The Animal Kingdom

The animal kingdom has general characteristics and its sub-kingdoms exhibit more specific characteristics. Imagine that you are an animal. What are your major concerns? Food, reproduction, and shelter, right? These are pretty basic, and you can see how a person who is connected to the animal kingdom might communicate these priorities in the homeopathic consultation. Appearance will be of prime importance due to the drive to reproduce, so the person will be carefully dressed, perhaps provocatively dressed. Hair will be important, and women may wear it long and highly styled. They may also unconsciously play with their hair. Men might choose animal skins to wear —perhaps a leather jacket. Women may wear prints that resemble animals, like a leopard or zebra. People who feel the animal nature will not want to appear older; in fact they may speak of their reluctance to age. Women past childbearing age and older men with an animal nature may still have an interest in appearing attractive. Now let us examine the animal sub-groups separately.

Mammals

Mammals are closest to humans and are easier for us to understand, in that we can perceive their emotional states. Some of the characteristics and qualities of mammals are: dependency, milk, fur, mother, need to hide weakness, group acceptance, loyalty to group, and being cruel to enemies.

Mammals have certain needs related to mothering and nurturing. It is important that young mammals have access to their mother's milk. Since there is usually competition for this milk within the litter, a young mammal will want to appear healthy and vigorous to encourage the mother to feed it. This may give rise to a tendency to hide weakness or deformity of any type—even in adulthood.

Mammals transmit the essence of their species through their milk. The relatively long nursing/dependency period allows the parent to communicate appropriate behavior and self-preservation techniques to their young. Because of this shared history with their mother, people who respond to mammal remedies will have some focus on mothering. It could be a memory of maternal neglect; or an overdependence on the mother; or a strong urge to be a mother. Almost all mammal remedies are made from the milk of the species such as the milk of the lion, elephant, dog, cat, horse, bear, cow, dolphin, wolf, and more.

This is a general overview of the common characteristics of mammals. To differentiate each animal's characteristics from the others is beyond the scope of this book, but, as you can imagine, the specific characteristics of the dog are quite different from that of the dolphin.

Insects

Insects are known for their industriousness and ability to work in groups. The members of insect groups are rather interchangeable, and relationships are not personal: they are based on function with the goal of achieving success for the whole. Success is defined as food acquisition or production; protection of the young; and survival of the group. They are hyper-alert to danger which can come in many forms. (Have you ever stepped on an ant?) The bee, ant, flea, butterfly, wasp, cockroach, and more are some examples of insect remedies. The following case illustrates how insect consciousness can be exhibited in a human family.

> A woman came to see me for a variety of complaints. When I inquired about her family, she proudly told me that she and her husband worked at the same factory—one worked the day shift and one the night shift. They had three school-aged children. When I made the comment that it might be difficult to manage family life with such a schedule, she clearly did not relate to my comment. She boasted about how organized the household was, and how she and her husband shared the big jobs, like cooking and cleaning. Everything was on a schedule, with each of the children having a specific way of contributing—one made lunches, one did laundry, and one made beds each day. Everything worked like a well-oiled machine—much like a hive in fact. She was not at all concerned that there was virtually no time for interaction as a couple or a family. This was specifically not important to her. She responded well to the remedy *Apis* (the bee), and began to think of ways her household could include more nurturing activities.

Spiders

Spiders are a highly specialized sub-kingdom of the animal world. They are characterized by mobility and sensitivity to sound and motion. Vibration is felt throughout the body, not just in the ears. People who need a spider remedy may enjoy travel, and may be focused on ideas of conspiracy or political intrigue. Such folks may prefer to take nourishment in liquid form rather than as a solid. People who are connected to spiders may love them or have an abnormal fear of them.

Some of the more well-known spider remedies are the black widow and the tarantula. There are many additional varieties. Unlike insect groups, spiders act in a more solitary fashion, connecting for sex and then completely disconnecting—even, in some instances, eating their mate after coition. Spiders have an important place as totems in mythology. There are many variations of the story of "Spider Woman" who created the world.

Birds

Birds are our messengers and enjoy freedom and lack of restriction. Birds' fast metabolism allows them to process food in flight. They are acutely sensitive to weather, to earth's electromagnetic field, and have good eyesight. Homeopath Peter Fraser states: "The freedom that birds (people needing a bird remedy) seek, and which they are thwarted in their efforts to attain, is most importantly an emotional one." (p. 21) Persons who respond to bird remedies think in concepts, not details. They are impartial and detached. They may have a sense of inner buzzing or vibration; and they may like open spaces and become restless and nervous if confined. Few people will have a conscious desire to fly, but they may be passionate to experience the freedom and lack of restriction that flying offers. What can cause such restriction? Parental rules, the responsibility of children, and illness, to name a few things.

Birds are highly sensitive to their environments, and to other beings. They may kill to protect their young, but they do not kill for sport. According to Fraser, people who respond to bird remedies often have a high degree of empathy and can be found in healing professions. Frequently, they deplete themselves in this work and succumb to collapse.

This sensitivity is expressed physically, too, in being highly attuned to sound, rhythm, and weather patterns. Birds also have very acute vision, People who need bird remedies, not surprisingly, may be thin and spare, even though they may have large appetites.

Some birds used as homeopathic remedies are the bald eagle, falcon, hawk, turkey vulture, raven, swan, great horned owl, and brown pelican. Usually some external part of the bird, such as a feather, is used to make a remedy. It is interesting to compare information about the bald eagle from both a homeopathic and shamanistic perspective. Ted Andrews, comments, "The fact that they are good at feeding themselves from the land and still soar to great heights in the sky reflects much about the hidden significance of the eagle. (p.136)

On a similar note, homeopath Jonathan Shore observes that eagles "move between the world of daily life and the world of the dream. The one informs the other, and the ability to participate in both is essential to their wellbeing." (p. 89) It is worth recalling that this strong eagle characteristic was elicited from those who participated in the proving.

Reptiles

This class of animals evokes strong emotional responses from most people. Snakes are often feared, hated, or found to be revolting. Or they may be revered as spiritual teachers. Yet, they share the same animal concerns for shelter, food, and procreating. However, they go about this in ways that seem strange to many. A snake appears in our oldest stories of paradise. Apparently, as it is told, all was going really well until Eve listened to the snake and ate from the tree of the knowledge of good and evil. This created a primary split, since we can assume that, prior to becoming acquainted with this dichotomy, the major blessing of paradise was unity or non-duality, Now it was split, and people experienced the polarities of good and evil; love and hate; jealousy and acceptance.

Snakes have a rather unique physiology; for example, the famous "forked tongue" is actually split. Some of their inner organs are often singular rather than double (one lung instead of two) and can be pushed to one side of their gullet to allow for the swallowing and digestion of rather large mammals. It's their venom, actually, that digests these very large meals. They do not need to eat very often —just a few times a year—but these meals are huge.

Reptiles have no metabolic heat function and must bathe in the sun to store warmth. Snakes are virtually deaf, although they are very sensitive to vibration, and use their transparent eyelids to scan their environment constantly. Most snakes are not aggressive unless provoked, despite the weapon of their venom. Some snakes have venom that affects the blood, while others are neurotoxic. Some snakes give birth to living young, but are known to abandon them in the nest. They provide no nurturing such as we saw with mammals and birds. Snakes grow until they die, shedding their skin at intervals as it becomes confining.

Remedies made from snakes include the cobra and the rattlesnake. These remedies are made from the snake's venom. Some of the characteristics we see in persons who need snake remedies are loquaciousness, sarcasm, a critical nature, alcoholism, deep spirituality, and depression with suicidal tendencies. On the physical level there can be deep pathology such as sepsis, cholera, and other blood disorganizing conditions. It is worth noting that the caduceus, the symbol for medicine and healing, actually contains two snakes.

Sea life

Resting at the shore, we

can experience the in-breath and out-breath of the waves. Whenever I go to the sea, I am reminded that this "breathing" goes on day and night, each day, regardless of whether I or anyone witnesses it. The tides also represent an in-and-out breath on a larger scale, reminding us, in a gentle way, that each force has an opposing movement. The sea is the birth place of life on this planet, and, in some ways, all humans recognize it as "mother."

While many enjoy seeing and even frolicking with large sea mammals, I have always preferred the opportunity to observe life under water. Snorkeling over schools of incredibly colorful fish that seem to move so purposefully, but so randomly, is, to my human eyes, delightful. Scuba diving or deep sea diving—coming eye-to-eye and shoulder-to-fin with exotic underwater creatures—has been one of the most thrilling experiences of my life. I felt every inch the intruder and, yet, every bit at home with underwater life.

The sea contains dissolved minerals, animals, and plant life. Only 5% is said to have been explored, and many species are unnamed and unseen. Remedies from the sea include fish, mollusks, sponges, starfish, dolphins, and a whale, among others; there are nearly 100 sea-based remedies available.

The characteristics of sea-life include lots of motion, safety concerns, a desire for privacy, and a need for somewhere to hide. Many fish desire to be left alone and fear invasion of their space or body. Persons who respond well to sea remedies may either love or fear being in the water, may desire or not desire fish, and may become irritable when required to respond within a relationship. After all, it is not in the nature of sea creatures to be highly responsive, communicative, or connected. Therefore, they may desire solitude more than others, perhaps nourishing their instinctual and creative life.

Sea remedy folks may have a high sex drive but not be interested in permanent relationships. Like insects, there is usually satisfaction in work and being busy and in motion. In some cases this includes a desire to dance. They may feel a deep connection to unconscious processes, but not be able to articulate them. In Chapter One, I summarized the wonderful examination of the remedy *Sepia* (ink from the cuttlefish), by Dr. Edward Whitmont. This remedy is often thought to typify sea remedies.

Some concepts, and therefore words, that characterize sea-life thinking are "flow," "inside my shell," "drift," "sink," "swim," "out-of-my-depth," "drowning," and "castaway." Persons who respond to sea remedies are generally inhibited in expressing feelings and cope best when alone.

Admittedly, this discussion of animals has focused on homeopathic remedies from animal sources. Power animals in Shamanism are known for their dramatic qualities—qualities that the sick person may lack or need. They also befriend the shaman and assist him in accessing the power of nature. Ted Andrews speaks of these beliefs this way:

> Animals have often been attributed with fantastic qualities, and, if nothing else, this attribution helps us appreciate the natural world more fully. Every animal is a gateway to the phenomenal world of the human spirit.... When we learn to speak with

> the animals, to listen with animal ears, see through animal eyes, we experience the phenomena, the power, and the potential of the human essence, and it is then that animals are no longer our subordinates. They become our teachers, our friends, and our companions. (p. x)

Reflecting on the words above, we cannot help but be reminded of *Animal Minds, Human Voices,* the book of animal provings by Nancy Herrick that prompted me to incubate, dream, and finally write this book. Andrews' dictionary of animal totems in *Animal-Speak* will fascinate any homeopath. There is a dramatic congruence between the qualities Andrews lists and the ways in which specific animal remedies are understood within homeopathy. Whether accessed through little pills or conjured through drumming and trance, animals hold powerful keys to understanding humanity and healing it.

Next we journey to a more placid world, that of Plants. You may be surprised to see how varied and powerful are the species made into homeopathic remedies.

CHAPTER SEVEN

The Journey to the Plant Kingdom

Plant spirit medicine is the shaman's way with plants. It recognizes that plants have spirit, and that spirit is the strongest medicine. Sprit can heal the deepest reaches of the heart and soul.

(Cowan p. 20)

~~~~~

In the Rose [Rosa gallica, Ancient Yellow Rose] proving, all the movements of the heart: loss, grief, rebelliousness, independence, compassion, danger, passivity, and love come to the fore.

(Herrick, Sacred Plants, Human Voices (p. 298)
~~~~~

Now we enter a world both dark and bright; both wet and dry; both small and large. Most of it lives within a few feet of the earth's surface—with roots tangling below and stalks and trunks reaching up. Specimens are relatively stationary and many species live in clusters. There is little violence here, except for the occasional vine choking off life from another plant in its attempt to survive. There is just a little carnivorous behavior too. There is, however, a sort of passive treachery in that some species can sicken and even kill an animal or person, and many more plants are irritants if they are ingested or even touched.

With few exceptions, land-based plants live in soil or sand, so a visit to their kingdom may involve getting one's hands dirty. All the human senses can be stimulated by plants—the beauty of color and form, the rustle of leaves, the scent of flowers, the coarseness of bark and softness of petals, and finally, the taste of edible fruits, vegetables, and herbs. It is as though nature produced this cornucopia in complete harmony and balance with humans and animals. It is said that there is no disease on earth that cannot be cured by a plant. It is also said that most of the plants on earth have yet to be catalogued to understand their specific contribution to the planet. One thing is certain however: they give freely and expect nothing in return.

But do plants communicate? There is a lot of recent research that demonstrates that they do. First they communicate with each other. Some typical experiments demonstrate that they release CO2 and nutrients through their complex root systems to other plants. Suzanne Simard demonstrates this in a fascinating TED talk available on YouTube. The impetus for her research was the inexplicable die-off of Douglas fir trees in Oregon after paper birches had been cleared from the forest. It seems that the birches had been helping their conifer neighbors. She was able to discover a vast mycelial network that connected both tree species. This has now been found to underlie all forests and is known as the "Wood Wide Web."

Plants communicate through the air also. They can secrete chemicals that deter predator insects. As soon as danger is identified by one member of the plant community, it sends signals to its neighbors to secrete chemicals that are lethal to the predator. Additional research has demonstrated that plants actually "hear" sound waves and produce them too. But why can't we hear them or understand their language? The problem may be with our conditioning, not with the plants' failures. Stephen Harrod Buhner says:

> It is very difficult to understand the language of plants if you cannot open sensory gating channels more widely....this...gating, trained into us from childhood, is why it is so often hard to see the meanings in the sensory communications that come to us from the natural world....(p. 280)

> When sensory gating channels are widely opened, the boundary between self and other thins....You know the reality of the interior life of the other solely in reference to itself...you can experience the life

> that occurs outside the human frame in its own terms—without using the human world as a point of orientation. (p. 289)

More and more experiments involve actually listening to the sounds of plants. In a fascinating YouTube video, we can see Simone Vitale use sophisticated electronic equipment to translate the sounds (frequencies) of a house plant's roots and leaves into what sounds just like music of the spheres. Damanhur is a commune, ecovillage, and spiritual community located in northern Italy. One of their more fascinating research projects involves synthesizing the sounds of plants into music, and this has been recorded for us on YouTube.

How do Shamans connect with Plants?

> Among many of the indigenous peoples of America, when a medicine person was invoking a plant for healing, its song would be sung and that would help focus the medicinal qualities of the plant on a sonic level.... As the song was sung once more, the singer would drop down through the reality of the song and let it speak through him...and as the reality of that song came once more into the world, the person hearing it...would in fact begin to experience the healing of the plant on a sonic level. (Buhner p. 388)

Eliot Cowan interviewed five shamans who use plant spirit-medicine to heal. Following is an excerpt from his interview with Don Enrique Salmon who explains how his own spirit plant helps him heal others:

> They (his grandparents) taught me how to get in touch with the spirits within plants...certain songs and certain ways to pick the plants and pray to the plants and the earth to bring out more of the medicine of the plant. [Eliot asks him if his spirit plant talks to him.] Yes, the root. The whole plant will talk, but I get more messages from the root. In order to talk to the root, you have to dig it up out of the ground, but it stays alive. It helps me figure out what is wrong with people. If I have a problem with a patient and am not sure what to do, I can go to (my spirit plant.)...I try to find a quiet place to relax for a few hours....I will drink some of the tea from the plant and get some of the plant itself. I'll wait for a dream, or I will hum a medicine song. I close my eyes and the spirit will come to me. (pp. 132-134)

Another shaman, Grandma Bertha Grove, describes her use of a sage plant to heal diabetic pain in a patient's legs:

> You just put it on [the patient's legs] and blow into it.... See the Creator and the four Directions, they are real powerful and they are supporting that sage, and you're supporting it too with your breath, because you are a spirit too. All spirits have to work together. (p. 176)

Plants and Homeopathy

Plants have a very long shared history with the human race. Plant remedies comprise the largest group of homeopathic remedies. Homeopaths know the messages of plants in the same way they know the voices of animals and minerals—through provings. Many remedies are made from poisonous plants and some from nourishing plants.

In order to survive, plants, which lack locomotion, must be placed in an ideal setting. In this setting, the proper amount of light, water, wind, and correct temperature will allow them to thrive. So we can expect to see a high degree of sensitivity in the person who responds to remedies from the plant kingdoms. This will be exhibited in sensitivity to temperature extremes, ailments arising from the elements (chapped face from wind for example), rashes developing from contact with ordinary substances, and sensitivity to odors and sounds. In general, plant people have a very sensitive nature on every level. Plant people also need certain conditions to feel comfortable. Like plants, their preoccupation will be in finding a place of comfort—the right amount of heat, wind, cold, sun, water, and light. They also have an emotional sensitivity and can be wounded easily. When wounded, they tend to isolate themselves and withdraw rather than express themselves or fight, as an animal or mineral person might do.

Many skin issues will result from contact with the elements and the environment. Sun sensitivity will be high, contact dermatitis common, and outbreaks, such as hives, can be expected. In fact, all sorts of allergies will plague the person needing a plant remedy, since allergies are nothing more than an excessive response to a benign substance. Some substances are not benign, of course, and plant persons will have a more exaggerated response to these than will other people.

When smoke contaminated the air of northern California in recent summers, it was interesting to observe the varying degrees of sensitivity people exhibited. Some wore masks all the time; some felt a burning in their mucous membranes; some experienced anxiety; while others seemed to be unaffected. Of course, though some people seemed unaffected at the time, the noxious components of forest-fire smoke can have long lasting consequences.

The organization of the plant kingdom

If it were not for the scientific classification of plants into categories, it would be much more difficult for the homeopath to map the plant kingdom when he travels there. "Kings Play Chess On Fine Green Sand" is a commonly used mnemonic for remembering the progression of categories in the plant kingdoms—beginning with Kingdom and ending with Species. The addition of Life and Domain is fairly recent and does not make for a nice mnemonic at all! (Little Dirty Kings Play...?)

The following illustration from Wikipedia shows how both plants and animals are organized scientifically. However, according to the same source, these divisions are somewhat fluid and are apt to be replaced with other classification terms. The important factor for the homeopath to know is that there are relationships among the many plants and therefore among the remedies made from plants.

How to make sense of these relationships has been explained in different ways by various homeopaths. Rajan Sankaran, a world-renowned homeopath from India, has shed considerable light on this problem by linking plants to miasms in his two volume work, *An Insight into*

Plants. Homeopaths' interest in plants usually begins at the family level. Dr. Sankaran has interpreted 22 families of remedies, exploring the relationship of the plants to each other and to miasms. Like many homeopaths, he was initially confounded by the inclusion of apparently dissimilar plants within one family. This required homeopaths to resort to rote learning of the symptoms within each family—not very efficient or useful.

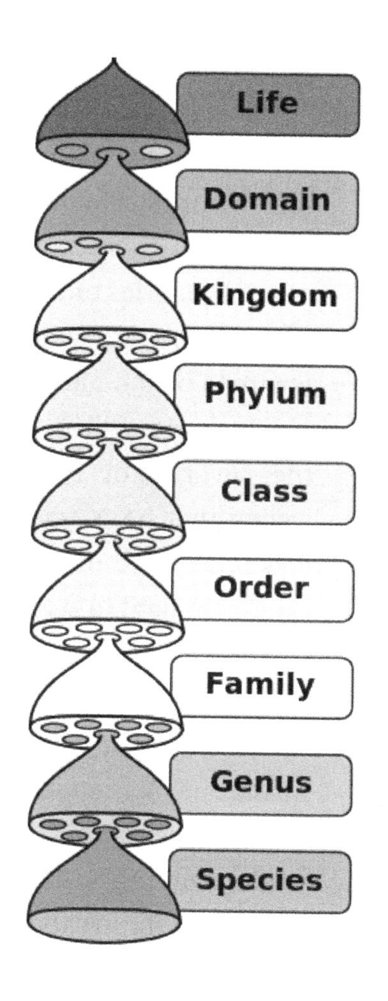

It is far beyond the scope of this book to begin to summarize the masterful insights of Dr. Sankaran. However, I will introduce his method through one family of plants—the *Compositae*. This word alone will not mean much to most readers, but if I tell you that it includes daisies and sunflowers, you will have a better picture. Most of us have had some experience using the remedy *Arnica montana*, the mountain daisy, for injuries. It is probably the most popular single remedy sold.

Arnica daisy

Physically, *Arnica* helps relieve pain from injuries, sprains, surgeries, head injuries, and virtually any other sort of physically induced pain. Unknown to most, it also has mental qualities too, most notably that the person who is injured wants to be left alone, and not be touched. He will even diminish the severity of his injuries by saying that he is not hurt, while it is obvious to others that he is! This is thought to stem from a fear of being injured further by another's ministrations. We classify *Arnica* in the Acute miasm because the injury has arisen suddenly (as opposed to a chronic injury like a bedsore), and the person believes he may be near death from the injury.

Arnica Daisy

Another plant in this family is *Chamomilla*. The remedy made from this plant is needed by people (children included) who are terribly upset by their misery—howling and complaining and crying. They may in turn injure others who attempt to help them by hurling objects as well as insults at them. We classify this remedy in the Typhoid miasm, where a person feels that, while they are terribly sick, they will eventually get better after a struggle. This

German Chamomile

is a typical pattern of Typhoid fever, which causes great debility and loss of bodily fluids. In fact, it is fatal in only 25% of people who are not treated. Modern treatment with antibiotics has significantly reduced the mortality rate, but the imprint of this way of reacting to disease and disorder is still strong within the human race.

Yet a third daisy in this family is *Bellis perennis*, a daisy remedy that is specifically used for injuries (including surgery) to the breast and other soft tissues in the abdominal area. It is invaluable in treating injuries sustained in an auto accident due to the over-tightening of the seat belt. It is classified in the Cancer miasm. Dr. Sankaran defines this miasm as having the feeling of weakness and incapacity and the desire to struggle beyond her limits. The person must succeed or death may ensue. Again, please remember that these are feelings or perceptions, not necessarily facts.

Gerbera Daisy
(*Bellis perennis*)

A fourth daisy in this family is *Taraxicum*, the dandelion. The remedy *Taraxicum* has an affinity for complaints of the liver, digestion, and kidneys. It is especially indicated for people who have a frequent need to urinate and pass copious amounts of urine. It is also good for bedwetting problems during sleep. This remedy is in the Ringworm miasm, where afflicted people alternate between struggling with feelings of doubt about their success and then give up, repeating the cycle over and over again.

I will now touch upon the main categories of plants that are made into homeopathic remedies. This will include vines, trees, nuts, desert plants, fruits, herbs, and flowers. We will end with the mushrooms, which, strangely, have recently been reclassified as animals.

Dandelion (*Taraxicum*)

Vines

If you have ever had an outbreak of poison oak or poison ivy, you may recall how distressing it was. You may even recall how restless you felt with the everlasting itching and scratching, and the tendency of the pustules to pop up all over your body and face with no seeming pattern. These restless behaviors are a key concept to understanding vines in general, and these two poisonous plants in particular. Vines love to move, and they will keep going—crawling over fences and barriers and under walls—to continue their self-expression and seeking. What are the plants seeking? Most likely they are looking for conditions favorable to their survival—water, light, sun, air, protection.

It should be no surprise that the remedies *Rhus toxicodendron* (poison oak) and *Rhus radicans* (poison ivy) are both made from these poisonous plants and are specific in healing the itching and rashes these plants impart to the unaware hiker or gardener. But this by no means covers their beneficial potential. They are also excellent for certain types of digestive as well as rheumatic complaints. For example, *Rhus toxicodendron* is healing to a certain type of arthritis where the sufferer experiences pain when he begins to walk, and then finds relief in continuing to walk.

Trees

Many homeopathic remedies are made from trees. Looking at the conifers, for example, we have remedies from *Arbor vitae* (*Thuja occidentalis*), hemlock, red cedar, Douglas fir, the redwood tree, and many others. A feeling of brittleness pervades these remedies. This can be in the mental sphere, as a fear of ideas or values being broken, or a sense of physical brittleness and susceptibility to shattering.

Arbor vitae (Remedy: Thuja)

Thuja is one of the most frequently prescribed remedies in homeopathy. It can be curative to almost any system or organ in the body as well as helpful in very specific mental and emotional states. Some of the strange mental symptoms include the certainty that soul and body are separated. The person who will respond to the remedy *Thuja* feels much worse in cold damp conditions, which can make him ill. The tree, incidentally, thrives only in well-drained soil. *Thuja* is popularly known as a cure for warts and as a way to mitigate the adverse effects of vaccinations.

Many remedies are made from deciduous trees also. One example is the red or purple willow (*Salix purpurea*), and there are many more.

Nuts

One of the characteristics of a person who will respond to a remedy made from the cashew (*Anacardium orientale*) is a very hard, even aggressive, exterior and a soft, more sympathetic interior. These traits often alternate as aspects of the personality. The reason for this is that the *Anacardium* person usually was severely abused in childhood, causing him or her to "harden." However, the natural tendency to compassion is never completely stamped out. In deciding which part to exhibit, the person may feel that they have "an angel on one shoulder and a devil on the other shoulder," each whispering ideas about how to behave or respond.

~

Desert plants

In *The Desert World, A Homeopathic Exploration,* Dr. Todd Rowe provides a summary of the conditions that affect all things living in the desert. (pp. 35-39) These conditions include a pre-occupation with water; torpor followed by intense activity due to the scarcity and then sudden availability of water; transformation and desolation; nomadic tendencies and fantasies; fear of or participation in ambush. On the physical level, desert plants are effective in treating cardiac conditions, edema, skin issues, and many other ailments. Desert plants lack the lush green color of plants grown in more temperate areas and tend to be spiny, thorny, and twisted. Each plant in the desert is a rare and unique structure rather than being clustered with others of their species. Many desert plants are highly poisonous to insects and animals, and even to small offshoots of their own organism! This is a far cry from the nurturing behavior that has been measured in conifers, for example.

Perhaps from this "heartlessness" we can infer why cactus plants are known to remedy cardiac conditions. *Cactus grandiflora* and *Cereus bonplandii* (a night blooming cactus) have effects on very painful heart conditions where it feels as though a hand is pressing or squeezing the heart.

Fruits and herbs

Mistletoe, potato, vanilla, cayenne pepper, peppermint, coffee, tea, onion, tomato, tobacco, St. John's wort, basil, mint, and many, many more familiar herbs and edibles are included among homeopathic remedies. Homeopathy is very often confused with herbalism by the members of the general public who are accustomed to using teas, oils, and tinctures of plants for their medicine. For the most part, however, there is no one-to-one relationship between the action of herbs and the indication for and the effect of the homeopathic preparation.

Sometimes there is a more unexpected connection. For example, the remedy made from coffee (*Coffea*) is used to promote sleep, especially if the sleeplessness has been caused by joyful news. This is an example of the Law of Similars, a homeopathic dictum that says: what the substance causes—in the case of coffee, exaltation and wakefulness—the homeopathic remedy will cure. But how do we explain the use of the remedy *Capsicum* (cayenne) to relieve homesickness? I believe there is a way to understand all these connections, but we may not know them yet. Still, we know that it is important to understand the natural history and form of a plant as part of understanding its action as a remedy. Fortunately, homeopaths have access to reference materials that contain the full discussion of how a remedy may be curative.

Flowers

Jasmine, rose, violet, pansy, periwinkle, rhododendron, and chrysanthemum just begin the list of flowers that are sources for homeopathic remedies. While we may wax poetic about the beauty of flowers, their deeper characteristics are often surprising. The remedy made from the shy, retiring Lily of the Valley, for example, is useful for people who are very irritable. The morning glory can cure suicidal thoughts. The Sacred Lotus, the very symbol of spiritual harmony, can be used to help those with violent, even psychotic impulses.

Nancy Herrick, in *Sacred Plants, Human Voices,* provides a wonderful overview of the varieties of lotus plants and their use in human history, mythology, and ideology, and attempts to explain the darkness found in the flower. "...the Lotus... represents the height of spiritual power." (p. 7) Yet, the conditions associated with the Lotus, such as violence and psychosis, are somehow held within this temple of apparent purity. Herrick compares it with gold (*Aurum*), the king of metals, and the cobra (*Naja*), the king of snakes, where the highest spiritual aspirations are mingled with the darkest human impulses. The journey to the plant kingdom, in search of the Power Plant, is fraught with more danger than we might have imagined!

Mushrooms

The mushroom or fungi kingdom has apparently baffled scientists and defied easy classification. It is now thought that mushrooms are closer to animals than plants. Mushrooms have no leaves, roots, or seeds and don't need light, so they're not a true vegetable. Animal-like traits include their dependency on organic matter created by other organisms and a cell wall that is made of chitin— similar to that of some insects and crustaceans. Mushroom undergrowth has now been found to link almost all above-ground plants.

Mushrooms are known for their culinary, medicinal, and psychoactive properties. They can be symbiotic with their hosts, feed on the decay of plants, or be parasitic. Massimo Mangialavori, a well-known Italian homeopath, has written a book about homeopathic mushroom remedies. He describes mushrooms as:

> ...recyclers, decomposing what is dead or dying in order to liberate nutrients.... In other words they transform the inhospitable into the hospitable so that plants can grow. In fact 95% of plants grow in symbiosis with fungi. They are life giving denizens of darkness, death, and decay. (p. xi)

The saying, "it just mushroomed out of control," has a basis in fact. Mushrooms can grow almost overnight to a huge size. Mangialavori says, "A single individual can generate the biomass of a whale." The largest living organism in the world is a mushroom in Oregon.

> Popularly known as the honey mushroom, the Armillariaostoyae started from a single spore too small to see without a microscope and has been weaving its black shoestring filaments through the forest for an estimated 2,400 years, killing trees as it grows. (abcnews.com)

People who need a fungus remedy are often rather other-worldly and unique. They do not seem to have concerns related to their strangeness but feel it as a familiar state. One famous character, Alice in Wonderland, certainly had some unusual experiences after ingesting mushrooms. Reading her story is similar to taking hallucinogenic mushrooms. I recommend re-visiting it as way to experience the power of the species.

Agaricus muscarius, the Amanita Toad Stool, is a typical homeopathic mushroom remedy. It is used to treat conditions that result from cold such as frostbite and chilblains as well as twitching and behavioral problems in children. It is the mushroom associated with Alice in Wonderland. Some other remedies made from mushrooms are *Bovista*, the puff-ball; *Secale*, a fungus that grows on rye; *Ustilago*, a corn fungus; *Cordyceps*, called the caterpillar fungus due to its appearance; and *Boletus laricis*, a type of white mushroom.

So we exit the plant kingdom through the mushroom door where things can become huge overnight and shrink just as rapidly. As Alice observed, things are getting *"curiouser and curiouser!"* Next we will visit the mineral kingdom, whose voice has been heard only by homeopaths.

CHAPTER EIGHT

The Journey to the Mineral Kingdom

Nature also forges man, now a gold man, now a silver man, now a fig man, now a bean man.

Paracelsus

Homeopathy is perhaps
the only system that has given voice to the
consciousness of the elements.

> Even in the case of the minerals, modern physics... gives us reason to wonder if perhaps some form of consciousness might not figure in the construction of reality. Quantum mechanics holds that matter may not be as innocent of mind as the materialist would have us believe. For example, a subatomic particle can exist simultaneously in multiple locations, as pure possibility, until it is measured—that is, perceived by a mind. Only then and not a moment sooner does it drop into reality as we know it: acquire fixed coordinates in time and space. The implication here is that matter might not exist as such in the absence of a perceiving subject. (Pollan p. 412)

For many readers, to attribute "power" to a mineral or metal may be stretching the magic-medicine analogy too far. We can experience the power of animals and recognize their attempts to communicate with, or at least acknowledge us as a species. Even plants seem to have some degree of sentience. But minerals? Rocks? Metal? These seem to be the very definition of inertness —meaning passive, immobile, still. Remember, however, that the same communicative animal or powerful plant is composed of the elements we consider inert.

Since we don't know precisely where consciousness exists, it could be that it is in the very physical web of an entity's molecules. Perhaps the strength of a lion

(*Lac leoninum* as a remedy) or the shyness of a larkspur (*Staphysagria*) derives directly from its chemical composition. Where exactly is consciousness? We think of consciousness as residing in or deriving from the brain, and the mind (whatever that is). Medicine now speaks of the microbiome—that heap of bacteria, viruses, and who-knows-what else that exists where the sun does not shine, in our gut—as a second brain.

A lot of the characteristics we associate with minerals have been attributed to them for millennia. For example, people feel a connection to their jewelry and their crystals—often far beyond the intrinsic value of the items. Value may be sentimental—like wearing a piece of jewelry that someone gave you or passed on to you as part of an inheritance. Somehow, we sense that some energetic frequency remains from the person who gave it to us, and this makes it very precious to us. Then, there is the popular belief in birthstones—the specific gem or mineral that is associated with our astrological sun sign. The American Gem Society says that "the origin of birthstones is believed to date back to the breastplate of Aaron, which contained twelve gemstones representing the Twelve Tribes of Israel."

There is a lot of evidence that the ancients, as well as the new thinkers, favor the idea that consciousness is universal. The "new" science of Panpsychism posits that everything has a mind.

> Consciousness permeates reality. Rather than being just a unique feature of human subjective experience, it's the foundation of the universe, present in every particle and all physical matter.

> This sounds like easily-dismissible bunkum, but as traditional attempts to explain consciousness continue to fail, the "panpsychist" view is increasingly being taken seriously by credible philosophers, neuroscientists, and physicists..." (Olivia Goldhill, Quartz, qz.com, January 27, 2018)

Gosh, this sounds a lot like animism, the belief system of many primitive people, dressed up with a new name. Wikipedia defines animism as:

> ...the beliefs that all material phenomena have agency, that there exists no hard and fast distinction between the spiritual and physical (or material) world and that soul or spirit or sentience *exists not only in humans, but also in other animals, plants, rocks, geographic features such as mountains or rivers or other entities of the natural environment, including thunder, wind and shadows. (emphasis added)*

Since animism is known to be one of the oldest worldviews, it is worth considering that our ancestors had a second sight, or some insight that we now lack, which, perhaps, has been systematically suppressed. The definition of Pantheism, also from Wikipedia, is that "Pantheism is the belief that reality is identical with divinity, or that all things compose an all-encompassing, immanent god." This goes a step further. Now, reality is not just conscious, it actually is the divine in form. Of course we don't know the nature of this consciousness, nor are we encouraged to discover or contact it in the elements—at least not in the present materialistic world. We cannot tap into the consciousness of any other person, either, but we must rely instead on some verbal or non-verbal communication to reveal the person's state or process.

One definition, found in the Google Dictionary, defines consciousness as "...awareness by the mind of itself and the world." Entire books have been written about the nature of consciousness, usually human consciousness or higher consciousness—the state where we rise above our base or animal nature to become aligned with more ideal impulses. But, let us return to the possibility that elements are conscious.

Shamanism and Minerals

In my reading about Shamanism, I found no specific mention of shamans relating directly to the mineral world and invoking its healing spirit. We can assume, however, since shamans connect to all of nature, that they are intimately aware of healing powers within rocks, stones, and crystals. Many photos of their altars show the presence of rocks, stones, and crystals. These are present, presumably, to enhance the ambiance of the sacred space through beauty, and power.

Homeopathy and Minerals

Homeopathy is perhaps the only system that has given voice to the consciousness of elements. This is actually quite wonderful to contemplate. There they are—rocks, and minerals, and salts—lying at our feet all these years, and we did not know what they were saying. Homeopaths know all too well the messages of the elements. How? The same way they have come to hear the voices of animals and plants—through "provings." When we make mineral and metallic substances into remedies and then give them to healthy subjects to determine what symptoms arise, we are actually raising a huge antenna to hear the voice of the mineral substance. Homeopaths know as much about the predilections, character, desires, sorrow, and nature of a mineral (person), as they do about any animal or plant that is included in the homeopathic *Materia Medica*.

In order to understand the minerals and homeopathy, we will need to revisit the periodic table—the table of elements that you may have studied in chemistry. Frankly, when I studied it, I was rather bored by it; the study and practice of homeopathy, however, has enlivened it for me. I hope to share a bit of this magic with you. (The periodic table can be found on the last page of this chapter.)

Perhaps the first thing to notice about the periodic table is the high degree of organization. Nothing strays; everything is in its proper place, row, and column. Then there are the numbers given to each element, as well as names, so that they will never, ever, be confused with each other. Elements are arranged from left-to-right and top-to-bottom in the order of their increasing atomic numbers. Atomic numbers indicate the number of protons in the nucleus and electrons in the shell of an atom. In fact, this is how the element gets its number. For example, Hydrogen has one electron, and its atomic number is one; while Mercury has 80, and its atomic number is 80.

The scientific names of the elements come from various sources. Why is Mercury called "Hg" in the table? Hg is short for *Hydrargyrum*, which is a Latinized form of a Greek word meaning "water-silver." Fortunately, most tables also print the common name of the element. Each row corresponds to specific electron shells; there is less similarity between elements in the rows than there is between the elements in the columns

Here is another interesting fact: The first 94 elements of the periodic table (up to Plutonium) are naturally occurring, while the rest, from 95 to 118, have only been synthesized in laboratories or nuclear reactors. A few questions arise in my mind about all this. How did scientists know to stop at 118? The answer, presumably, is that beyond 118, the nucleus becomes too heavy for stability. Also, why are two rows, those beginning with 57 and 89, relegated to the bottom of the chart—off the chart, to be precise? I can see that they might not fit well into their rows, but could there not be some other arrangement? I am sure that some more scientifically oriented readers will know the answers to these puzzling questions.

Despite these questions, there are plenty of known facts and elements for homeopaths to study within the first 94 elements, where many have been proven and are in common use as remedies. We will see that minerals have very specific identities when they "speak" through people.

The Voices of Minerals

So what characteristics can we expect to find in a person who will respond to a mineral remedy? Recall that "animal people" are dramatic, and concerned with reproduction, food, and shelter, and sometimes with nurturing and protecting their young. "Plant people" we found to be very sensitive to their environment and highly reactive to it, in fact. Factors like temperature, wind, and contact with other substances through their skin or ingestion can cause reactions. Their moods can be quite easily affected and changeable, but they are usually not aggressive or threatening as an "animal people" remedy can be.

If you needed a mineral remedy, what would you be like? First and foremost, you would want to know your place, since that defines you. You have no particular need to seek food or change your environment. In fact, structure is paramount, i.e., order, time, and precision in dates and numbers. You are organized, and may even be fastidious; you are proper and like to follow rules; you are systematic, concrete, and logical. You like security, and dislike change. Duty and responsibility come naturally to you. You are pragmatic, and fit well into military and religious institutions as well as government. Certain professions come to mind that will be comfortable for you: accountant, scientist, security professional, or government worker. Your clothes will resemble uniforms even if you do not wear one because pragmatism, not flowery comfort or attraction, is your concern. Instead, you may favor checks, plaids, and stripes. They do echo the design of the periodic table, after all!

What makes the health of a mineral person break down? Change is the number one stressor. That can mean a new location, more responsibility, and unexpected environmental factors. Breakdowns can occur as a result of what, in the world's terms, is a good thing. This might include a promotion or the opportunity to travel.

A special word needs to be said about salts. Salts are the combination of two elements, an acid and a base, that results in a compound that is highly stable. In fact, at least one of the elements in a salt could not exist alone and must combine with another in order to be stable. A simple example is table salt or sodium chloride. In homeopathy, this compound is called *Natrum muriaticum* and is a remedy that is often prescribed. It has many applications, but one notable use is to help people express their grief. Persons who will respond to this remedy tend to keep a "stiff upper lip" (as though it were salted) and to be reluctant to let tears flow. Often the loss suffered by this person was in the breaking of a bond or contract. Remember that salts exist only because of a union of two elements. Examples of broken contracts can be divorce, an empty nest, or legal issues. The person cannot cry for fear of losing salt! *Natrum muriaticum* will soften their wall. You can see how the inner state reflects the outer state of the salt.

Another element with a powerful and clear picture is Silicon (*Silicea*). Silica is the "grit" of the earth, providing form and strength, first to plants, and then to animals who consume them. The person who needs Silica will be missing this grit or strength both physically and mentally. Babies walk late; adults can be yielding and easily follow the directions of others. There are a whole host of related symptoms that make this mineral remedy one of the deepest acting and most frequently prescribed.

The Elements and Miasms

The elements relate to the miasms, as well, with a general deepening, or becoming more of a serious miasm, from top-to-bottom and from left-to-right on the periodic table. Both Gold (*Aurum*) and Mercury (*Mercurius*), for example, are in the syphilitic miasm, where the most serious physical and emotional states can be found. Mercury, in fact, was an early treatment for syphilis—one that did as much harm as good, unfortunately.

Columns have chemical similarity among their elements. Using column 17, for example (a list of elements called the Halogens), we can understand the progression of pathology as we go down the column by giving the main theme of each remedy.

Fluorine – is concerned with leaving or being left
Chlorine – fears being abandoned because of the grief it will cause
Bromine – fears being attacked by someone
Iodine – fears being stabbed in the back or in the throat (Iodine is an important remedy for thyroid issues, and the thyroid is in the throat)

I will review a few of the most commonly used mineral remedies as a way of sharing their voices. It will perhaps surprise you to learn them.

Calcarea carbonica is a remedy made from the oyster shell. Hahnemann thoroughly understood its importance in forming a foundation for strength and functioning. Its primary physical action is to allow the body to assimilate calcium. No matter how much calcium the person ingests, they will still be deficient if they need the remedy *Calcarea carbonica*. In infants this deficiency will show up as late teething and walking, as though the structures are too weak to support them. In older children and adults, we will see weakness from almost any stressor, such as walking upstairs or feeling a cold wind. Similarly, their emotional state overreacts to the idea of rats, robbers, disease, and other imagined threats. They will worry, withdraw, and refuse to increase their responsibilities for fear of overtaxing or revealing themselves. We can well imagine the oyster, stuck in its shell, preyed upon by hungry fish, rats, and birds, and unable to escape. Its only defense is to close its shell! Such people are bound to have a difficult time in life, especially, modern, western life, unless treated with this remedy.

Sulfur is another of the macro minerals, like Calcium —those found in abundance within the body. Whereas *Calcarea* dealt with basic issues of standing, walking, and functioning, *Sulphur* signifies the rudimentary development of ego strength. In *Sulphur* we find a need for acknowledgement and appreciation of one's mind, works, and projects. Children reach this stage, however rudimentary, when they begin to seek approval from parents or teachers. Receiving this recognition leads to the development of a sense of self. So far, so good. For the person who needs *Sulphur*, however, there is a deep fascination with projects and endeavors that, to others, are either too difficult to understand or are seen as trivial and ill-conceived. Yet the person who needs *Sulphur* is completely absorbed in and fascinated with their creation to the extent of neglecting hygiene and social conventions. We call this person a "ragged philosopher."

Moving up the developmental ladder, we can discuss *Magnesium*. This element is found as a salt rather than in pure form. Note that *Sulphur* stood alone as a remedy and as a mineral. Because of its need to combine with other elements, we can assume that relational issues are central to people who benefit from *Magnesium*. It is actually concerned with a special relationship—that of the mother or nurturing. *Magnesium* has been described as the "orphan remedy," and those who need it may have had experiences of abandonment. This can be as simple as being overlooked, as in the "middle-child syndrome," or the child who is least liked in a family; it does not necessarily refer to physical but rather to emotional abandonment. These are gentle folk, and they will use pleasing and peacemaking as a way to gain attention; but it never gets them what they need. After treatment with a *Magnesium* salt, they will still be gentle and sympathetic, but will have learned to internalize self-care and will cease seeking approval in the world.

Metals are a special class of minerals. They are concerned with performance, strength, defense, and function, and they give form to our world. Some are also important to our metabolic processes, such as iron (*Ferrum*). The person who may need lead (*Plumbum*), might express a lot of the symptoms of lead poisoning—developmental delays, incoordination, sluggish digestion and elimination—regardless of whether or not they have had such poisoning. Aluminum (*Alumina*) is frequently, but by no means exclusively, used for conditions in aging and premature aging, such as poor memory, dryness of skin, and constipation.

From their dark places under the earth or their invisible place dissolved in dirt or water, minerals, metals, and the elements find their way into our lives and bodies. Taken up by plants and animals that we eat, they sing their song within our cells and bodily fluids to maintain our strength and to balance not only our physical processes but our emotional and mental activities as well.

In the next chapter, we will examine how we inherit our characteristics. We will also review the new genetic research, which not only goes beyond the Mendelian laws, but actually supports Samuel Hahnemann's understanding of inherited disease.

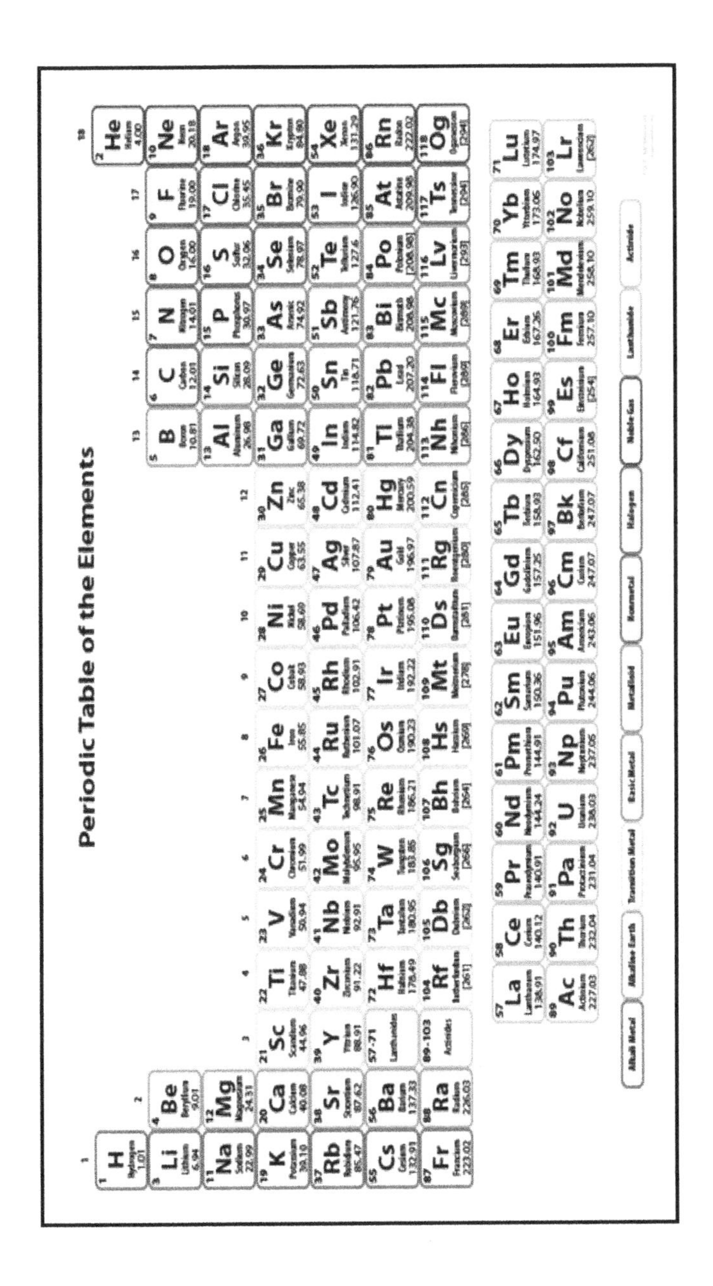
Periodic Table of the Elements

CHAPTER NINE

The Ancestors

For I, the Lord your God, am an impassioned God,
visiting the guilt of the fathers upon the children,
upon the third and upon the fourth generations.

Exodus 20:5

To readers in their reproductive years, I want to suggest that homeopathic or shamanic treatment before you conceive can spare your children from suffering in the same ways you have suffered

Within homeopathy as well as shamanic traditions, the person who needs healing is viewed as someone connected to and influenced by their ancestral network. Shamans may encounter the spirits of ancestors on their journey to the spirit worlds, whereas homeopaths ask questions about lineage to determine the types of health conditions that run in the patient's family. This information can give clues to miasmatic tendencies—the inherited predisposition to disease. The client himself will often provide clues to his miasm by revealing specific interests, ways of thinking, speaking, and, of course, the type of illness he presents.

Whether shamanistic or homeopathic, the work with ancestors involves clearing unhealthy physical, emotional, and mental tendencies. Many patients I have seen are marked by childhood experiences of abuse or loss, from which they have never recovered. These experiences may also occur later in life within adult relationships, but they almost always reflect early childhood events.

Many patients say that the parent who abused them was herself abused as a child. In this way, we witness the handing down of energetic patterns and tendencies. The beauty of homeopathic treatment, and, I presume, shamanic treatment is that these memories and tendencies can be eradicated from the person's psyche and body, thereby sparing future generations.

Not all that is inherited is bad, of course. It is worthwhile exploring one's lineage to discover patterns of strength and health as well as positive habits and messages. Many people feel the benevolent presence of a grandparent or other deceased relative guiding them and watching over them.

There seem to be three main ways we understand our genetic makeup. First, there is the human genome project —the discovery by scientists of how many genes we have and what operations each one controls. Many view this work as woefully incomplete, since we seem to have a lot of genes for which no purpose has been found.

Second is our ability to access resources, such as Ancestry DNA, which uses some of our genetic material to uncover information about our past. Such research often results in finding living relatives—bringing the search for the past right into the present.

Third is the newly energized science of epigenetics —the promise that we can actually modify our genetic expression through environmental factors such as diet and lifestyle. In fact, the latest research asserts that only a very small percentage of diseases are gene-linked.

Epigenetics has revealed some very provocative findings regarding inheritance. First, in studies using animal models, it has documented the father's contribution to disease in future generations. Second, a mother's prenatal exposure to strong emotional situations has been shown to affect the fetus profoundly. Third, any number of these impactful situations can affect many future generations—making the quote from Exodus prophetic. Most epigenetic studies have been done with animal subjects in order to quickly track the changes that occur through several generations. It remains to be seen whether humans will exhibit the same characteristics the experimental animals do.

> The field of epigenetics is quickly growing and with it the understanding that both the environment and individual lifestyle can also directly interact with the genome to influence epigenetic change. These changes may be reflected at various stages throughout a person's life and even in later generations. For example, human epidemiological studies have provided evidence that prenatal and early postnatal environmental factors influence the adult risk of developing various chronic diseases and behavioral disorders. (*Epigenetics and the Environment: How Lifestyle Can Influence Epigenetic Change from One Generation to the Next,* whatisepigentics.com)

The following summary of the impact of the father's use of tobacco on the development of ADHD and autism to the third generation in mice is very disturbing.

> Dads who smoke could be sentencing their offspring—and the offspring of generations to come—to cognitive problems, according to a new study of mice. When male mice were exposed to nicotine, their offspring showed signs of a mouse version of attention-deficit hyperactivity disorder (ADHD), as well as abnormal behavior and learning impairments. (Reported in the e-newsletter, *The Natural Society, December 22, 2018*)

Although our genotype, or genetic makeup, is decided when we're conceived, the way we interact with our environment and the lifestyle choices we make can alter the epigenetic sequence over time. It can dynamically change the way in which our genes are expressed.

But what if a big, overall change is possible—something beyond changing the "writing" on a gene? Could homeopathic treatment, which is known to produce healthier people, actually manipulate gene expression to be more supportive to the organism? It's a lot to suggest, I know.

One proxy for health is age of death. It is not perfect, but it is some indication of health. Let's go back to the example of the British Royal family. As noted earlier, Dr. Peter Fisher, a homeopath, was physician to this family for a number of years, as were other homeopaths before he was retained. Think what you will about the royals, but there is one incontrovertible fact: they live long lives. The Queen Mother, mother of Queen Elizabeth, passed away at 101. Queen Elizabeth is now 92 and still performing her royal duties. Alongside her is Prince Phillip, who is 97.

Royal interest in homeopathy spanned the ocean. Many European monarchs from countries such as Germany have been known to use homeopathy. Because the House of Windsor had strong links to Germany, it seems likely that the strength provided by homeopathy has been instilled in the genetic pool for generations. A most interesting and comprehensive discussion of the royals and homeopathy can be found in Dana Ullman's book, *Why Famous People and Cultural Heroes Choose Homeopathy*. The Royal family is no more nor less important than anyone else. I mention them because it is easy to see how they may have modified their health destiny by using homeopathic treatment.

How do ancestors affect our health? The most obvious way is genetics—as discussed above. Another way is through beliefs and values. Most families have strong taboos and equally strong requirements regarding behavior. To be effective in controlling family members, these values must be impressed upon children from a very young age. Often this inculcation of beliefs and values is very strong in immigrant groups who wish to preserve the way of life they bring from another land. The family members carry a strong code of comportment that is nearly as irrevocable as the genetic code itself.

Within some cultural traditions, deceased ancestors are considered to be a part of the family and are believed to have the power to intervene in the affairs of the living. Another way that the young can be affected by elders is through prenatal exposure of the mother to harmful substances or environments. Radiation, toxins, cigarette smoking, drugs or alcohol can all alter the traits inherited by the fetus. Less measurable, and less measured, are the direct effects of good exposure, such as to meditation, music, nature and harmonious feelings.

Recent research in the area of epigenetics confirms that Hahnemann's understanding of miasm as an energetic rather than a biological transfer was accurate. Let us remember that he postulated this over 200 years ago. The understanding now is that the Mendelian laws of inheritance, asserting that traits are passed on only through sexual reproduction, are limited. Indeed. It has been known for some time, for example, that the offspring of Holocaust survivors, who were conceived and born after their parents' liberation from camps, often exhibit post-traumatic stress disorder.

What Do Miasms Mean to the Homeopath?

There are now ten miasms—or underlying tendencies to disease—recognized within homeopathy. Their names will seem strange to the lay reader, but each miasm has a different degree of seriousness, a unique pace in disease progress, and a wide variation in the subjective sense of desperation in the patient. I have given an example of how a few of these miasms manifest in various remedies in the *Compositae* family in the plant kingdom in Chapter Seven. The ten miasms and their brief description are listed below. It is impossible to give a full picture of a miasm in such a short list, but readers may want to pursue more in-depth descriptions such as are found in *Miasms of the New Millennium*, the most up-to-date and comprehensive book on miasms.

Acute – The patient has a condition from which he will recover quickly or it will kill him. Sudden onset, panic, high fever, and shock are some of the characteristics of this miasm. Prolonged states include PTSD. Arnica is an acute remedy that is used by many for injuries.

Typhoid – The patient has a feeling of urgency out of proportion to the situation. He wants to go home to bed, and he may think about that all day and then collapse when he gets there. It is named after Typhoid fever which has a rather slow onset and is characterized by periods of wellness and relapses.

Malarial – So named because the patient, as in malaria, never feels really well between the episodes of disease or problems. These patients are very disconsolate and complain a lot.

Psoric – These patients are optimistic and focused on overcoming external problems. Though they may be troubled by skin conditions, they recognize that both their diseases and any failure they may experience are not life threatening.

Ringworm – This is a slow paced miasm, and the diseases within it are slow to appear and slow to disappear — if they ever do. They are not life threatening and the patient is truly patient about their resolution.

Sycotic – Persons in this miasm feel that something about them is shameful, and so they try to hide it. Perhaps in compensation, their body often produces excesses such as warts and discharges.

Cancer – Again the outer appearance is at odds with the inner dynamic. The person in this miasm is a perfectionist who needs to control and excel, while the disease of cancer is a manifestation of chaos and dysregulation. Many other diseases besides cancer can affect a person who has the Cancer miasm.

Tubercular – These people are romantic, and passionate about life and everything else — travelers, risk-takers. They are speedy and impulsive and they may eventually burn out and succumb to respiratory infections or other diseases that result from their lifestyle.

Leprosy – These patients, just as lepers in the past, feel that they are unworthy and disfigured in some way and are outcasts from society.

Syphilitic – This is the most destructive and, indeed, the most dangerous miasm, where we find suicide, murder, and all sorts of emotional and physical extremes—and, sometimes, the highest manifestation of spirituality.

How does an understanding of miasms help homeopaths achieve a cure? When we cannot obtain the expected result from a certain remedy, we must look to a possible underlying miasm—and we can treat *that* with a specific remedy known to cure miasmatic influences. After these remedies take effect, the remedy more specific to the current disease state can be prescribed or re-prescribed and it will usually result in a complete cure.

When you ponder it, this is actually an amazing discovery. The understanding is that the miasmatic tendency toward disease is so strong that it becomes a type of disease in itself. It is so overpowering that the current disease state cannot be fully eradicated without completing this deeper cure. Hahnemann was the person who postulated the effects of miasms in his two-volume work, *Chronic Diseases*. His insights into the inherited tendency to disease and the subsequent development of disease states are nothing short of brilliant.

So how might a person inherit a miasm from a parent or grandparent? A few examples will help clarify this. A child born into a very unstable home with severe economic problems and the need to relocate frequently, combined with the parents' fear of the law, a landlord, or other external forces would tend to live in an "acute" state all the time. This might be characterized by unrelenting feelings of fear and panic that could last well into adulthood.

Another example is a child who is reared by shame-based parents. She might be brought up in a religion of guilt, sent to a religious school, and be told that no matter how hard she tries she will never be good enough. "Good" can mean clean, smart, clever, pretty or any other quality that a Sycotic person feels they lack.

> I recall a patient who came to his appointment at my office asking for help before he "killed someone." He was so prone to road rage that he knew it was just a matter of time before he killed or was killed. Sure enough, his childhood had been characterized by abuse—especially in the evening and at night. Needless to say, he had a lot of trouble sleeping and was on many anti-depressants and sleep medications. Oddly enough, this man had been in a helping profession his whole life! I was able to find the remedy that helped him release his anger and focus on finding new meaning in his life.

A person who was consistently abused physically will tend to store rage in their body and psyche and develop feelings of revenge for years before they can escape their abusers. Once free, they will likely seek to hurt others.

Shamans and Ancestors

From my reading in Shamanistic literature, I know that the familial context of the patient is equally important to shamans. Many times it seems that the spirit of the ancestors is contacted directly to eliminate the tendency to disease that they may have transmitted to the patient. Although shamans may not delineate the types of influences affecting the patient as homeopaths do, they surely have an intuitive sense of the varying degrees of severity in inherited disorders.

Our new understanding of genetics and inheritance gives new meaning to the Iroquois tribe's injunction to consider the welfare of seven generations when making any decision. Originally understood to refer to environmental decisions, we now know that all our lifestyle choices can have long-lasting effects on offspring for many generations. To readers in their reproductive years, I want to suggest that homeopathic or shamanic treatment before you conceive can spare your children from suffering in the same ways you have suffered—whether physically, mentally, or emotionally. In this way you will give them not only the gift of life, but the gift of health at every level.

CHAPTER TEN

The Homeopath's Patient

The patient's uniqueness
is the precise key to their healing.

~~~

The engagement of the will for health is
the greatest effect of the correct remedy.
~~~

The patient is what this is all about. Why journey or go into trance or communicate with powerful nature spirits if there is no sick person? Unfortunately there is an abundance of them. Presumably there was no sickness in the Garden of Eden. Whether this paradise lasted for millennia or just the lifetime of its two famous inhabitants is unimportant. What is important is noting that illness is now considered part of the human experience, and we are born and bred to accept it. I imagine that visitors from a more advanced civilization might take a look at our sniffles and surgery and consider our situation quite barbaric—as it is. We take for granted that we will break down from time to time, beginning with the colds and colic of infancy. We have insurance, sick days, health plans, medicine cabinets, and all sorts of accoutrements in place to support what we believe to be our inevitable and periodic collapses. Supposedly women continue to endure Eve's curse to bear children in pain (how did they get them previously I wonder?), and it seems that the entire race now participates in that curse of pain and suffering.

There are degrees of sickness. Acute illness comes on suddenly and usually leaves of its own accord. This includes all 200 colds and the many strains of influenza. Related to these are coughs, sore throats, bronchial conditions, pneumonia, and other short-term, and, in some cases, serious conditions. Chronic conditions are just that—chronic, and it is expected that they will never go away and they will need medical treatment forever.

Mental illness is an especially challenging and heartbreaking condition because the person, unlike one with an acute or chronic condition, is really not himself. Delusions, paranoia, and mania may twist the mind until the original person can no longer be contacted.

Developmental and behavioral conditions are heart breaking to the patient as well as their family. Emotional conditions, like depression and anxiety, are highly distressing because the person who has these, unlike many with mental illness, is acutely aware of their condition, but often unable to find relief.

Injuries are yet another category of suffering. Auto accidents have wreaked havoc on so many bodies, as have falls from bikes and horses. Sports injuries can also have serious and long-term effects.

Yet we homeopaths insist that the organism wants to be healthy, and that symptoms are messengers that signal that something is wrong. Symptoms are nasty, annoying, and painful, and most of us want them to go away and stay away. We rarely think to express gratitude for their letting us know that something needs attention. They serve an important function—they make us get help. Often that help is in the form of conventional medicine where silencing symptoms has become synonymous with cure. But it is far from that. In homeopathy we know that suppressing symptoms will lead to deeper disease. The organism says, "Well, you did not want to listen to my telling you how distorted your immune system had become when you had an allergy, so now I will turn up the heat and give you asthma—or worse."

While we may be better at defining disease than health, it is worth trying. Health, as we have all heard, is more than the absence of disease. It is vitality, energy, the ability to engage in one's profession or passion. I consider a healthy person to have three characteristics: first, sufficient energy for their daily tasks; second, the ability to sleep well; third, sexual energy appropriate for their station in life. Whereas celibates don't need much or any sexual energy; married folks need some. These may seem very simple and basic, but ask yourself how many people you know who are good on all three counts. Ask yourself if you are.

Another hallmark of health is freedom. We are each unique, and the real art of life is in finding our freedom in that uniqueness, embracing it rather than attempting to change it. We are who we are and will never be very different from our core temperament and conditioning. But are we free from unresolved guilt, grief, abuse, and abandonment wounds? As adults, are we still trying to please living (or dead) parents? Can we take reasonable risks or engage in some novel pleasures and pastimes?

Consider, for example, a person who wants to walk in the woods but cannot do so. If the limitation is a bad knee that is scheduled for knee replacement surgery, that person is still potentially free, for they can walk in the woods after surgery. If the reason for not taking the walk is due to a frightening experience the person had in the woods when she was a child, that person will *never* be free unless they resolve that issue or have homeopathic or perhaps shamanic healing. If the person cannot walk in the woods because of a fear of snakes, that person also will not be free until they undergo aversion therapy or homeopathic or perhaps shamanic healing.

You may be surprised to learn that homeopathy has the ability to heal deep fears and memories, but it can do so. In fact, that is where it shines. It can easily take care of a sore throat or diarrhea, but the power of homeopathy is in its ability to deeply heal the psyche.

Can it really take care of everything? I believe homeopathy can address many of the ills of mankind, but it cannot make lost organs or limbs re-grow. That said, I personally don't treat cancer for two reasons. One is that it is a felony in California to treat cancer with anything other than chemotherapy, radiation, and surgery. It is immaterial whether the person gets better with alternative medicine or how many waivers they sign, it is still a felony. That means jail time. Secondly, the symptoms of cancer are not always strong, and many times the cancer is discovered through tests rather than noticeable changes. For example, a woman with an ovarian tumor may not have symptoms, but she has a disease whose process needs to be monitored through blood tests and scans—two things I am not qualified to order or interpret. This is too risky for the patient. I recommend that such patients seek a medically trained homeopath.

A patient I am reluctant to take, but sometimes will, is someone taking a number of prescription drugs. Why? Because prescription drugs suppress the ability of the vital force to engage in healing. The vital force is the innate power in all of us that keeps us healthy or returns us to health when we are off balance. It is also called energy and *chi*. When the vital force has been tamped down, as it invariably is with prescription drugs, there is less energy available for healing. These patients, if they choose homeopathy, need to be treated in a slow and steady way, and must often work with their prescribing doctor to wean off drugs. I warn them that if they tell the doctor they are taking homeopathic remedies, a rather unpleasant scene can take place, including the doctor's refusing to treat them any further. Yes, this does happen.

Constitutional Treatment

The model of care that I am describing is called constitutional care which, for the way I practice, entails getting to know the patient very well and prescribing one remedy at the correct potency to stimulate healing. Preparing to see the patient, I review the intake form well before the appointment, looking for themes, unusual items, anything alarming, and inconsistencies, and I note entries to explore further during the meeting.

Homeopathy is based on individualized treatment. Even if several people have the same condition, they will each need a different remedy because they experience their condition differently. This concept is utterly different from the approach of conventional medicine where treatment is tailored to the disease rather than the patient. In fact, we homeopaths do not care that much about diagnosis.

This must seem like heresy to those accustomed to the energy, sometimes obsessional, that is expended in conventional medical circles to name the cause of the suffering. Homeopaths are much more interested in how the patient experiences the suffering.

Patients are not accustomed to the precise and compassionate way we listen to them, and they always like it. They know that their suffering is personal and unique, but few conventional doctors are interested in learning about the way it affects the patient. As homeopaths we know that the patient's uniqueness is the precise key to their healing and to our finding the correct remedy. The correct remedy is a perfect match to their suffering and symptoms. Yes, making this match is a very subtle process. Success requires our being well-trained and well-motivated to undertake the journey to the power source in nature that is seeking the patient even as the patient and homeopath are seeking it.

Homeopaths are trained to notice the most subtle cues to each person's uniqueness. This can include style of dressing, hand gestures (or lack thereof), tone of voice, way of speaking, tendencies to flatter, and the words they use—apologetic, critical, or blaming—and much, much more. Actually we consider each of these traits as a symptom, since, in our homeopathic world, a symptom is simply an outer expression of the internal world. It does not need to be painful. Looking at behaviors in this way helps us to be immune to any insults or other social transgressions that the patient may send our way.

In the next step in working with the patient, a homeopath will try to find a theme or pattern in their life. We all have these patterns but many of us are unaware of them. Typical themes include struggle, hiding, accidents, tragedies, abuse, loss, abandonment, paranoia, loneliness, good fortune, frustration, travel, reversals, illness, criminal behavior, confinement, and more.

You will recall that when we described the kingdoms of remedies, we talked about traits that might identify a person as needing a remedy from an animal, plant, or mineral source. Themes will offer more clues to the nature of the patient and help us find the remedy match. Most people are unaware of the distinctive way in which they express themselves and the uniqueness of their worldview. After all, we live with these characteristics and beliefs our whole life, and they don't seem strange to us!

We are all unique

One map of our uniqueness that many of us are familiar with is our astrological picture, in particular our birth or natal chart. Even if you don't know your chart in detail, you probably know your sign, which tells where the sun was in the zodiac at the moment of your birth. The entire chart shows the relationship among the planets and the zodiac signs at the time of our birth. It also shows how these elements will relate to 12 aspects of our life, called the houses, such as childhood, family of origin, work, relationships, partnership, and fortune, to name a few.

Doing the math of the relationships among these variables leads us to produce our natal chart, our fingerprint of destiny. It is unique to the extent that a natal chart is duplicated only once every 26,000 years!

What kind of questions help us elicit the unique experience of the patient before us? We start where they are—with their suffering, their symptoms—and ask these types of questions:

1. When did it start?
2. What was going on in your life when it began?
3. How does it feel (type of pain)?
4. How many areas are affected? For example, some people with rather modest pains can actually feel suicidal while others bear terrible pains without complaint. It is important to note that we do not prefer one response to the other—but rather are interested in knowing which response the person has.
5. What makes it better or worse? Heat, cold, outdoors, breezes, wrapping up tightly? These are just some of the ways that suffering can be alleviated. Again, we are interested in what is, not what should be.
6. What times of day make it—and you—feel worse or better? Some people wake up sluggish; others well rested. Some love sunsets; others feel depressed in the early evening. All these preferences are yours and they are not likely to change—nor should they
7. Which side of your body is affected? Believe it or not, some folks are almost always injured, pained, or affected on one side more than the other. Various

remedies are known to work better on either left or right sided complaints.

What can be cured?

When considering a patient before us, homeopaths look at a phenomenon called "the totality of symptoms." This means that, while we are interested in the rash or pains the patient has consulted us about, we are also interested in how and when this started, what mental or emotional strain has been a contributing (if not primary) cause, and all the other symptoms that may be reported during the consultation. In this age of medical specialization, patients are trained to limit their complaint to one item. The dermatologist is interested in the rash only, not in the job stress, or moldy home environment. Not so the homeopath. We want to heal the whole person. This phrase, whole person, is bandied about so freely that it has lost real meaning for most people. We are interested in the spiritual, mental, emotional, and physical disturbances of the dynamic force. The reason we are interested in the dynamic force is because we understand that that is where disease begins. Failing to bring balance here will result in disease suppression and eventual recurrence.

How successful are we?

This is a difficult question to answer. One of my instructors in homeopathic school shared that he had done an audit of several years of patients. Success was defined as getting the correct remedy on the second try. His success rate was about 88%. After many years of practice, I conducted a similar audit of my results and was please to find a similar level of success. Of course I wanted 100%, but I did not achieve that.

What limits our success as homeopaths? There are several factors. First is the person who wants to prove that homeopathy is ineffective. They will be able to do so. Patients do not need to be believers, but they need to be open in order for this sensitive medicine to work. If they signal their unconscious to reject homeopathy's efficacy, the unconscious will get the message. I have had several patients like this, but I did not detect how deep was their need to prove me and homeopathy wrong in the beginning of our work together. What types of patient might try to prove that homeopathy is ineffective? One typical situation is a husband who has been almost literally dragged to my office for help. "Fix him," is the wife's silent message. If this man does not want to be helped, he will not be. It *is*, however, ok for a patient to be skeptical as the anecdote below shows:

> In one of my administrative jobs, I worked with a colleague, trained as a clinician, who made no secret of his disdain for homeopathy. One day, however, he confessed his frustration at having lifelong post-nasal drip, and asked if there were a remedy for it. I suggested he go to the health food store and buy a particular remedy in the 30C potency and take it as needed. I had no

> contact with him for two years. The next time we spoke he said that he had pretty much changed his mind about homeopathy, and now saw its value. "Why?" I asked. "Because that remedy you suggested worked really well. I needed only one dose and have had relief ever since."

He was a non-believer but that did not block the action. There is a big difference between a skeptic and a blocker!

The second reason a person may not have results is because the homeopath did not prescribe the correct remedy. This is beyond frustrating for us, but it does happen. Sometimes we prescribe the correct remedy on the second meeting. Sometimes we never get it right. I have always welcomed study groups or sharing with colleagues where we can talk about these "difficult cases." It is amazing to see how quickly a colleague can see what I missed and suggest a better remedy. The third reason is even more confounding. We have made the best prescription and still the person does not respond. I don't know how to explain this in human logic. It may be that it is not time for the person to heal, and any attempt will fail. I do not like how powerless this makes me feel, but I have come to realize that it is a genuine phenomenon, not an excuse—and one that cannot be determined at the beginning of my relationship with the patient.

Our spirit wants us to be whole, and will ceaselessly communicate with us until we are. Homeopathic treatment may open the door to other forms of healing. Someone may need psychotherapy or somatic body work to release core wounds. However, they may be more likely to find a therapist and participate in the process after homeopathic treatment than before. Similarly, dietary changes that may improve their health will not be made until after the correct remedy is taken and the will to be truly healthy is engaged. This engagement of the will for health is, perhaps, the greatest effect of the correct remedy.

We homeopaths laugh (among ourselves) at the frequency with which a patient, who has experienced a profound cure as a result of taking the correct remedy, will say something like, "I don't think it was the pills that helped, but rather the reduced stress I have as a result of changing jobs." We wonder that he does not recall how terrified he was of changing jobs before he took the remedy. Indeed, the remedy has "cured" his fear and further improved his life.

How does healing happen?

Most of my patients have multiple conditions that need to be addressed. They may suffer from depression, hot flashes at night, arthritic pains, and insomnia. My task is to find a remedy that can address all of these. But in what order will they heal? The order of healing often surprises me. The vital force alone decides. It may be that a recently developed symptom will resolve first. It may be that the most serious symptom, in this case depression, will lift quickly. And, to my surprise, it may be that a symptom not even discussed during the interview will heal first. The patient will happily tell me that she is no longer constipated, although she failed to mention it at the first meeting! It is very common for old symptoms to reappear briefly and then resolve under the action of a constitutional remedy.

The remedy acts for a long time, so we must wait to see what will happen in the first six weeks or so—and then beyond that. This is also difficult for patients to accept—the long acting nature of treatment. Since most conventional drugs are taken daily, the idea of a single dose working for months can be confounding. Usually healing is subtle, but sometimes it's dramatic. I consider the healing I experienced and described in the Preface to have been dramatic.

The world knows when one has been healed. My patients report this phenomenon all the time—other people react to them in new ways after they have been treated homeopathically. It is as though family and friends (and enemies) detect a change and adjust themselves accordingly—usually in more positive ways. Michael Harner speaks of synchronicity in shamanic healing also, and this seems related to that phenomenon.

Shamanistic healing—at least as it is practiced in western circles—has many similarities with the homeopathic consultation and the goals and outcomes seem to be very similar. The next chapter will provide an overview and some detail on this process.

CHAPTER ELEVEN

The Shaman's Patient

By helping others shamanically, one becomes more powerful, self-fulfilled, and joyous....The enlightenment of shamanism is the ability to light up what others perceive as darkness and thereby to see and to journey on behalf of a humanity that is perilously close to losing its connectedness with all its relatives, the plants and animals of this good earth.

(Harner p.139)

Shamanic Healing

How deeply can shamanic treatment affect a life? In Shamanism the goal is to understand core wounds and transform self-limiting beliefs. The goal of a shamanic healing is to help recover a sense of personal power and restore the patient's ability to live freely. Once connected to the powerful healing source—whether an ancestor, animal, or plant—the patient can use this as a vehicle to maintain a connection to their higher power and experience ongoing evolution and healing. This is similar to the promise of the effect of the correct remedy in homeopathy.

The implication is that the shamanic journey is powerful enough to provide a thorough remediation of the patient's core illness as does homeopathy. Kalweit describes the depth and comprehensiveness of shamanic healing this way: "Shamanic therapy means the healing of an entire life rather than just healing failing functions and disruptive pains. For shamans, healing involves philosophy. A view of life." (p. 3) He continues:

> Primeval medicine and primal healing methods travel the inner way, in a quest for wholeness and health beyond the ego. The medicine of the shaman knows no pills and shots, does not seek to eliminate symptoms—that would go against nature. Rather it revives life and heals

> our relations with the world—for is illness not the clogging of our spiritual pores, a blockage of a global perception of the world...? (p.2)

Speaking of the deep mystery and invisibility of healing, Kalweit says:

> Healing does not come from the visible world, but from the invisible shadow world. This is the world to which our subtle-material body belongs, our energy body. Its visible form is the physical body. This shadow land is the homeland of shamans, where they 'operate,' give 'shots,' and 'medicine.' We know little of this land, the quantum realm of the holy. The things shamans say about it are metaphors, images that have been run through the brain and filtered through it. (p. 241)

Just as homeopaths do, shamans also recognize the uniqueness of their patients. Michael Harner tells us that, "A true master shaman does not challenge the validity of anybody else's experiences. The master shaman will try to integrate even the most unusual experiences into his total cosmology.... The master shaman never says that what you experienced is a fantasy." (p.45)

There are master shamans and less successful ones. Some work only on their families while others are available to the whole community. This is similar to the way homeopathy runs the gamut from self-care to professionalism. Shamans are evaluated by their community whose members have direct experience of success or limitation in the shaman's work. Michael Harner states:

> Only a few shamans become true masters of knowledge, power, and healing. There is typically a great deal of critical evaluation by the people in their communities as to how proficient particular shamans are, how successful they are in healing people. ...so, although many people can become shamans, only a few are recognized as outstanding. (p. 46)

Presumably, for shamans, some factors limiting their success might be their lineage, their training, their innate abilities, their experience as well as their dedication to their work.

I have personally not been treated shamanically, and have had to find sources that describe the shamanic healing process as well as results in clear not metaphorical language. Western sources are more available and provide the type of detail that make this mysterious process a bit easier to imagine as well as understand. I found a wealth of information on the website of Elizabeth Clemants, a shaman who practices in New York. She has a master's degree in Social Work and a minor in Law. She also practices as a mediator and conflict resolution coach.

She describes the work of a shaman as seeing a person's energy and then being able to shift it, bringing about a resolution to the patient's conflict or pain, regardless of the level on which it is manifesting. She has trained in western shamanic as well as Peruvian traditions and settings. Much of the following material is taken from the website elizabethclemants.com

She lists many reasons why a person might visit a

shaman. These include depression, relationship issues, insomnia, cancer, and addiction to name a few. She says that some people, upon hearing of shamanic healing, are drawn to it immediately. Others are not drawn to it and should not feel impelled to try it. For those who do visit her, this is what they can expect:

> At the beginning of a shaman session, clients will be asked to summon up a trigger, something that is emotionally 'charged'; anything that causes stress, unhappiness, difficulty, sadness, anger, or similar issue will suffice. A trigger doesn't need to be a big thing or a comprehensive run-through of your life's traumas or low points, although it should be a current strong feeling. You don't even need to say it out loud. It is sufficient for the client just to feel something that is currently charged for them —and sometimes it is easier to get in touch with the emotions if you visualize it rather than try to explain it aloud. Once you have pulled the charged feeling up to the surface, it will manifest as heavy energy. I can observe its effects, search for its true source and work to get rid of it.

Where is the person located in a Shamanic healing session? In homeopathic sessions, we sit—both the practitioner and the patient. Not so with Shamanism. Clemants continues:

> You may stand for a brief period of time while I work but most of the session you will be laying down on a massage table, face up, fully clothed. I may lightly touch you at times, but mostly will work on the energy around your body without touching you physically. Your job will be to

> breathe, and let me know how you are feeling and what is coming up for you as the session progresses.

Her website information says that a session lasts for one and one half hours—very similar to my homeopathic consultation of two hours. Regarding results, she claims that one session is sufficient for most of her clients, although a few may need an additional session for things that surface later. "The symptom that called them to a shaman in the first place (or another healing practitioner) turned out to be just the doorway into their journey, and on-going treatment from a shaman may be a part of that path."

Recovery from a session may require three days and include "feeling spacey or tired, feeling aches or pains in joints or muscles, crying off and on, or just feeling more sensitive than usual." She emphasizes the value of detoxing baths, light food, rest, and the avoidance of stimulants.

I was particularly struck by the similarity of her description of how clients might feel to how I perceive patients to feel after homeopathic treatment. She also speaks of the need to wait a few months to let all the changes manifest. The emphasis on subtle changes within the person that evoke notice from others is almost identical to my description of a similar phenomenon in the last chapter.

> Some clients walk out of a shaman session feeling lighter and better right away, while others need days or even weeks to notice the shifts and changes that the treatment had on them. It may only be in retrospect that you realize that

> something is different, that something shifted. You might notice that a relationship is in fact different, or that you are responding to your world with more lightness. Some clients don't even notice the concrete changes in themselves and feel the same, yet report that others have remarked that they seem to have changed....

Like Alan Waugh, whose work is described below, Clemants offers ongoing coaching sessions for those who need help and support going through changes in their lives after their Shamanic healing. The service I offer that is somewhat analogous to that is my Health Turn Around work with patients who are taking a considerable number of prescriptions drugs. Because I want their vital force available for eventual homeopathic healing, and prescription drugs diminish its availability, I help patients substitute herbs or supplement for their medications whenever this is a wise and safe choice. Sometimes I find that a less toxic medication is available, and they can then ask their prescriber about obtaining it. This form of coaching precedes the initial homeopathic consultation, rather than extending after it.

To find out more about the healing process in shamanistic treatment, I interviewed Alan Waugh, a Peruvian-trained western shaman with many years of experience. He observed that Shamanism is the "grandfather of holistic healing," meaning, as I explained regarding homeopathy, that the goal is to produce healing at the deepest level. It also means that the physical, mental/emotional, and spiritual aspects of the person will be healed if the treatment is successful. According to Alan, immediate effects are often, but not always, experienced. He said that he is more interested in how the person is three months after the treatment, and whether or not they have been able to make the life shifts that will maintain their health.

To assist western patients to adopt changes and anchor them into their lives, he usually suggests follow-up processes such as mentoring. Such work may uncover the patient's unconscious attachment to his chronic illness, which needs to be addressed before healing can succeed. In contrast, he notes that members of an indigenous community can access the shaman as frequently as needed, and also that follow-up work using other modalities is not part of that culture.

We can see the similar possibilities for the patient, whether undergoing homeopathic or shamanistic healing, to experience profound integration. There is a possibility for deep healing—one that will continue for some time, and it may take a while to fully manifest. The gift is that both systems offer the chance to redirect a life on a healthier path, on every level.

Between the patient and the healer is nature, which accomplishes the healing. In the next chapter we will look more deeply at how and why nature cooperates so beautifully with both practitioner and patient.

CHAPTER TWELVE

Spirits in Nature

Plant spirit medicine is the shaman's way with plants. It recognizes that plants have sprit, and that spirit is the strongest medicine. Spirit can heal the deepest reaches of the heart and soul.

(Cowan. p. 20)

The art of healing comes from nature, not from the physician. Therefore the physician must start from nature, with an open mind.

Paracelsus

I feel certain that Samuel Hahnemann approves of this book. I feel that, in fact, he inspired it, and watched over me as I developed the ideas. Because if he did not, I really don't know how it was born fully formed in my imagination in Mt Shasta. I was able to develop the entire outline quickly as part of a speech I delivered at the Wesak Festival in May, 2017, where I was invited to speak even though my subject was a real stretch for the theme of the conference.

In the past it was easy for me to dismiss Samuel Hahnemann's life based on his maverick, outspoken temperament, his frenetic escapes from the medical authorities with his wife and nine living children and, presumably, their household belongings perched on horse drawn wagons. It presents almost a comical scene if it were not so heartbreaking. His outspoken, less than diplomatic criticism of medicine further enhanced my picture of him as a roiling wave, tossing small ships around on a big sea. And yet, there is so much more.

I have had his writings, his few books, on my shelf for decades. A while back I tried to sell them, but there were no buyers. So, in trying to understand Dr. Hahnemann better, I took them down and read some of his original words. In these words, I found the intentions and motivations of someone closely connected to his own Soul and so responsive to its stirrings that he was impelled to fulfill his destiny despite the effect on his income, family, reputation and all he held dear.

At times I have been more than impatient with the world's reluctance to appreciate and accept homeopathy. I hoped for big changes in society during the seventies, but things reverted to the same old system, somewhat freshened by the civil rights movement and generally more open society. Then we hoped that the millennium would bring a new world order where freedom, equality, and renewed appreciation of nature were the hallmarks. Not much changed. The year 2012 was said to be tied to the Mayan calendar cycle, and new energies would be released that would transform our world and take out the dark forces that we now recognized as opposing all the wonders and freedoms we sought. Oh, well. Now some of us hope for a shift in 2020; others predict ongoing wars and struggles. I have come to terms with the need to do my best and make my life meaningful—one of service and creativity—regardless of whether the Age of Peace or the Golden Age dawns during my lifetime.

But imagine how Samuel Hahnemann must have felt. His life's work, his deep understanding of nature as a curative force was ridiculed, opposed, and criticized. His philosophy and practice held the seeds to transform medical practice and, with that, sustain and advance the health of the world's entire population. Things have taken (in my opinion) a profoundly wrong turn since his death, with the disparagement and dismissal of homeopathy in all the halls of government and commerce. I can only hope that he did not foresee this during his life. In his first published work, *Materia Medica Pura*, he offers this optimistic view of the future of medicine:

> The day of the true knowledge of medicines and of the true healing art will dawn when physicians will trust the cure of complete cases of disease to a single medicinal substance and when, regardless of traditional systems, they have investigated one single medicinal substance whose positive effects they have ascertained... (p. 2)

I am glad that his second marriage provided him some comfort and pleasure and even a thriving practice in his later years. Perhaps from his place beyond, time is not so important, and he can rest in peace knowing that some day his ideas will flourish. I believe that the spirits of nature will bring them back as homeopathy is finally validated as the potent, ecological, gentle, and effective method of healing that it is. George Vithoulkas, one of the most prominent living homeopaths, has summarized Hahnemann's understanding of homeopathy this way:

> It is governed by the laws of nature. It is a beautiful, simple, and completely effective system of medicine. It is, in fact, truth itself in healing. It acts in such harmony with life and the natural order of things, that it is a part of that order. It does not act upon nature; it is the very action of nature in the domain of healing. (p. 8)

What is Nature?

Every person has their own idea of what nature actually is. For some it is abstract; for others it may be romantic; some will call to mind a special animal or stream or seascape. Perhaps the drama of the arctic or desert shapes and shadows speak strongly to you. I suggest that nature is bigger than all of this. That it is a system, ever changing and eternal, with laws and components and processes that are grander than any design we can imagine. It operates within our bodies and on mountain tops. The models of the solar system and atomic structure look very similar—as do repeating designs all throughout the natural world. Nature folds in on itself in DNA ribbons and exerts tremendous force through the elements. It is not a cuddly little lamb, although that is part of nature; nor is it only a devastating wildfire. Paracelsus tell us: "Man is a microcosm, or a little world, because he is an extract from all the stars and planets of the whole firmament, from the earth and the elements; and so he is their quintessence."

Let us focus on the radical notions that George Vithoulkas expressed above. First is the idea that nature is active in healing. We can go a step further and say that the laws of healing are embedded in nature, and no true cure can occur outside these laws. Hahnemann described some of the laws of healing. First, that "like cures like." Homeopathic medicines are made from substances that are related to the symptoms the patient is expressing. Another law of healing is that the cure will go from the inside to the outside. A person with a fever and a rash will most likely experience the fever abating before the rash is cured. Obviously the fever is a bigger threat to the organism than the rash. Next, is healing in reverse order of disease onset. A homeopathic remedy can heal past diseases as well as present ones, and patients often find that they have a brief experience of old symptoms after taking a remedy. This brief experience is the opportunity for an older disease to be cured while the currently experienced disease is also cured. It is indeed humbling to witness the power of nature in resolving virtually every imbalance with one remedy.

Healing with Nature

I think there are also more subtle and unseen laws of healing with nature. First we must respect nature's role in our healing. In an earlier discussion I differentiated between a skeptic and a person who wishes to prove themselves above nature healing. The latter will not be healed by either Shamanism or homeopathy. The Laws of Karma figure in here also, and they are natural laws. If it is not our time to be healed, if our path requires more learning through suffering, we will not be healed. Our sprit knows this, and will speak to our unconscious about our path at this point in time.

> A dear friend of mine, now deceased, was born with a congenital heart condition which impacted her whole life. She had knowledge of a previous life where she had been part of cruel experiments on living subjects' hearts, and knew that this was the reason for her current condition. Despite this, she became a healer and model to many students and friends. While

> she died earlier than might have been expected, her life was a wonderful example of working to atone for her past life crimes while living a positive and purposeful life. Many therapies, including homeopathy, made her life easier, but there was no total cure.

If it is it true that what we seek is seeking us, and some remedies are made from substances as apparently as inert as minerals, then we must posit a force, an intelligence in every aspect of matter. Beyond this, I would attribute benevolence to these substances even if their behavior seems violent. Yes, a jackal will kill a lion cub, but that violence is within its nature and does not contaminate its place or presence in the natural order of things.

We homeopaths have all had the experience of suddenly knowing the remedy that will cure the patient. It comes into our minds, *but I think its sprit enters the room ahead of our cognition*. Perhaps the patient brings it in with him, they having had a long, if unconscious, association.

"Hello, homeopath: Camphor here; do you feel my cold breath?"

Or, "Belladonna here; do you feel my heat?"

"Lady Lion here; do you see how quiet and watchful I am in the hunt?"

Michael Harner talks of patients dreaming of the same animal or plant that the shaman approaches in his journey. One patient I treated, a neighbor, walked a few steps back to his home and told me later that he already felt much relief in every symptom by the time he opened his front gate. He had not yet ordered nor taken the remedy. In fact, I had not told him the name of the remedy, because I wanted to do a little more study to be certain it was the best choice. Yet, it found him.

Another story was told by one of my instructors. He knew the remedy that would help his patient, but, in writing the prescription, he wrote the wrong remedy name. The patient ordered and took the remedy and got completely well—by the spirit of the correct remedy, speculated my teacher.

Spirits in Nature

What does it mean to say that everything in nature has a spirit? Many belief systems hold that each plant, tree, flower, crystal, and animal has its own guardian spirit. Perhaps it is these spirits that communicate the essence of the entity they guard and are able to adapt their messages to the receivers. Many ancient societies worshiped nature, trees in particular. It was forbidden to make even a small cut in the bark. Trees were (and still are) planted at the time of a new birth, and it was understood that the tree and the young human life were entwined.

Plants have auras as do humans and animals. Stunning Kirlian photography images can be found on the internet. The humanist Rudolf Steiner posited that the auric field of a plant or tree contains the energy or life force that invites it upward and outward into greater growth, and that this aura is most alive in the spring. The authors of *The Secret Life of Plants* summarize the experience of earlier experiments in plant communication and offer this touching vignette:

> While electroding his plants, Sauvin gradually realized that like Vogel, he could obtain the best results from plants with which he had established a mental rapport. This he would accomplish by putting himself in a light trance, wishing the plant well, tenderly touching or washing its leaves, til he could feel his own energy emanations entering and interplaying with those of the plant. (p.37)

The famous botanist, Luther Burbank, developed an intimacy with plants that allowed him to develop many new species through his tender communication with them. He said, "The secret of improved plant breeding, apart from scientific knowledge, is love." In one vignette, while attempting to develop a spineless cactus, he tells the plant that spines are no longer necessary because he will protect the plant. (Tomkins and Bird, p.133) In a lecture, titled, "How to Produce New Fruits and Flowers" delivered to a scientific group, he said:

> In pursuing the study of any of the universal and everlasting laws of nature, some conditions are necessary before we can become one of nature's interpreters or the creator of any valuable work for the world.... Listen patiently, quietly, and reverently to the lessons, one by one which Mother Nature has to teach.... She conveys her truths only to those who are passive and receptive. Accepting these truths as suggested, wherever they may lead, then we have the whole universe in harmony with us. (Tomkins and Bird, p. 134)

Animals, according to recent research summarized in a National Geographic issue, *Inside Animal Minds*, published in 2017, are now known to have many characteristics in common with humans. These include intelligence, feelings, and the ability to form relationships. We already know that some primates as well as dolphins use language, and some birds mate for life. However, this research contains some surprising findings about fish, cockroaches, and voles, for example. Following is a summary of some of their findings:

> Much of what's so important to our own lives —memories, emotions, relationships, the daily experience of making plans and solving problems —is found all around us, and not just in obviously brainy creatures like chimpanzees or dolphins or crows, but even songbirds and fish and insects. Our experience of the world is far the richer for it. We live in a world of minds. Only some of them are human. [p. 5]

The quality of empathy was also found to be displayed in animal behaviors. There are incidents of one animal feeding a hungrier one, and adult animals, both male and female, coming to the rescue of abandoned eggs and young. Perhaps when they are called to share their special powers with ailing humans, the animal group or over-soul responds out of empathy and caring. Perhaps when they are distilled into a homeopathic remedy, this empathy, encoded in the nanoparticles of the liquid that medicates the pills, is alive with a beating heart of healing.

Shamans have protective spirits, typically animals, and many minor spirits to help with special situations. The power animal guides the shaman on his journeys to the other worlds and helps him return safely. Then he must provide a healing for the patient. It is known that each of us has guardian spirits to protect us in a world of hazards and dangers. One way we can each be more shamanistic (and perhaps better homeopaths) is to endeavor to meet our guides and work with them more consciously.

> It is really not the shaman at all, but the spirits who are doing the healing work.... becoming a shaman is also a matter of the spirits. You are not in this alone... far from it! In fact, the shaman is almost secondary.... It is not the shaman, but the spirits who have the only power that ever allowed any shaman throughout history to effectively catalyze a healing or discern a divination. Moreover, it is the spirits who choose the shaman... not the other way around. It is the spirits who decide who they work with, and it is entirely up to them whether they chose to stay, or not. (Steve Serr PhD, *Shamanism-101*)

There are differences as well as an essential unity between homeopathic and shamanistic healing. Nature is the underlying unity and power, although the way she is accessed and brought into form is different. The homeopath's pills are the breath of the shaman, and each encodes the power of nature. Our patients take them into their mouths; the shaman breaths healing into the patient's body. In each case we hope for the deepest healing, the most transformative experience for the patient. In each case we have done no harm, and, perhaps have done the greatest service to the patient. As each life radiates out to its immediate contacts and to the world, we have contributed positively to a more sane and holy environment. A Japanese shaman said it very succinctly in a way that is both humble and expansive—qualities both homeopaths and shamans can understand:

> I have given you a glimpse of seiki, the vital life force. You should not live without it. It brings true fulfillment to your life... Thanks to seiki, we can maintain our health and embrace each other peacefully, respectfully, and forgivingly. It brings about a generous frame of mind...The door to seiki is open to anyone who wishes to enter. Ikuko Osumi, Sensei. [Connor p. 266]

Addendum

Homeopaths and Shamans Heal the World

The model of healing I have described so far in this book is that of one practitioner and one patient at a time whether service is rendered by shamans or homeopaths. However, both shamans and homeopaths participate in healing projects on a larger scale. While I am not familiar with all of these projects, I wish to describe a few. They offer creative ways to heal many more people, including those who would not have the opportunity, or perhaps the inclination, to approach these practitioners under ordinary circumstances.

Homeopaths Heal the World

Jeremey Sherr is a world renowned homeopath and educator who, for the past ten years, has operated an HIV/AIDS treatment program in Tanzania, using homeopathy to treat people there and in 16 rural outreach settings. In some cases his treatment is the only treatment for the disease; while in other cases he blends homeopathy with more conventional medication. His work encompasses teaching, writing, and training indigenous people to become community-based homeopaths. His workforce is composed of volunteer homeopaths and homeopathic students as well as local residents. He also supplies food and nutrient support. Learn more and donate: homeopathyforhealthinafrica.org.

Another amazing program is being conducted in San Francisco and the South Bay Area by a group of homeopaths who offer free treatment at four locations to homeless people and veterans. Their non-profit organization—The Homeopathy Institute of the Pacific—has the motto: "Serving the Underserved and Those Who Have Served." Their work is supported by Hahnemann Laboratories of San Rafael, California, a respected manufacturer of homeopathic remedies that donates free remedies to these clinics. They plan to offer webinars to instruct people in how to open and run such clinics. Contact them or donate to their effort at homeopathyip.org.

The organization Homeopaths without Borders (hwbna.org) sends homeopaths to areas or communities where homeopathy is generally not used or where natural disasters have created a health crisis. Haiti is still being served by this group, whose members worked tirelessly after the earthquakes in 2010 and 2018. A current project is training birth attendants in Haiti to incorporate homeopathic treatment to mothers and infants in an attempt to address the extremely high infant and maternal mortality rates.

Homeopaths are also responding to areas in California where wild fires have left many homeless and distraught. The Camp Fire in Paradise, California, prompted one of the largest coordinated responses from homeopaths. They worked alongside other health professionals and the Red Cross to treat people who lost their homes, loved ones, pets, and community. The non-profit, Integrative Healers Action Network, received a grant from the Red Cross to continue developing a coordinated response to future disasters in California. As volunteers, they previously offered assistance to Sonoma County during the wildfires in 2017 as well as the Camp Fire in 2018. Their mission is "to provide acute and long-term care to communities impacted by emergency situations by providing integrative healing modalities through systems that bridge medicines and organizations." Their projects include services from naturopathic doctors, massage therapists, chiropractors, as well as homeopaths

What can homeopathy offer disaster victims? There are remedies that can help people cope with grief, shock, injuries, and loss, as well as treat the opportunistic infections and diseases that arise when normal sanitation and water systems are disrupted. The homeopaths who worked at the Camp fire found that they were required to respond to even more complex needs since many victims had lost their regular pain or other medications, and needed support for their chronic conditions. While we hope shamans can subdue the violent forces of nature (see below), it is wonderful to know that natural medicine and support will be available if and when needed.

Shamans in the community

A new arena for shamanic work relates to healing the larger community, bringing the power of the helping spirits to issues such as violence, conflict, or environmental pollution as well as threatened natural disasters. More and more frequently, shamans are called to respond to natural disasters and use their powers to communicate with the forces of nature to calm floods, fires, hurricanes, and winds. We in the west have dismissed this type of relationship to nature as being "primitive" and question its usefulness. Yet, these forces are made of the same molecules as our bodies and, if we believe in the unity of life, we can contact them. Perhaps some day we can tame them before they bring destruction.

> If this mysterious power is actually present in all things and beings, in thunder and lightning, in the breath and in the glance, would it not make sense to conduct ourselves in relation to natural phenomena as shamans do? Should we not feel awe toward these forces and secure their power for ourselves? (Harner pp. 232-233)

In one innovative program in Merced, California, Hmong shamans interface between the hospital and the Hmong community who are not familiar with nor trusting of western medicine. Cross cultural sensitivity has been significantly enhanced through this program with resulting improvement in the Hmong population's health status.

Shamans aided in the aftermath of 911 in a very unusual and esoteric way, described below:

> We are fortunate to have dedicated individuals in our midst who are working with the spirits in order to rectify the imbalance in Harmony brought about by the terrorists' actions. One example of this, psychopomp work (the conducting of souls), is underway by individuals and drumming groups across the land in order to restore balance disrupted by the sudden, violent deaths of the thousands of victims of this atrocity. We applaud these loving healers who swiftly began to work for the victims in a non-ordinary way, even as police, firefighters, and volunteers worked for them in the ordinary way. (*Healing the Aftermath of Terror*, Bill Brunton, Editor, *Shamanism*, Fall/Winter 2001, Vol. 14, No. 2)

Finally, there is, IM4US, while neither strictly homeopathic nor shamanistic, whose mission is:

> Integrative Medicine for the Underserved is a collaborative, multidisciplinary group of people committed to affordable, accessible integrative health care for all. Through outreach, education, research, and advocacy, we support those dedicated to promoting health in underserved populations. Together we work to shift the current paradigm towards equity, wellness, prevention, patient empowerment, and self-care. im4us.org

My apologies to the many selfless healers, both homeopathic, shamanistic, and others who work in projects that did not come to my attention in time to be included in this book. We look forward to a day when the violent side of nature is less destructive, and we may offer natural and gentle healing to those who are still suffering.

~~~ Acknowledgements

First, honors to Maria Lodes, of Lotus Editorial Services, who, with a very sharp pen, was often able to turn an awkward cluster of words into an arrangement as smooth as a lake on a calm day. She is at (marialodes.wixsite.com/lotus)

Next is Catherine M. Preus of Four Wild Geese Design, who used her artistic sense and much patience to create the cover and interior design and layout of this book. (FourWildGeeseDesign.com)

Ben Tasner gave everything a final coat of editing with his careful proof reading, wonderful suggestions, and encouragement.

Peter Mt Shasta, a spiritual teacher, author, and homeopath, offered feedback from a collegial perspective that helped me see beyond the borders of my original thinking in several instances.

Helga Alessio, Vice President of Quality Assurance at Hahnemann Laboratories, San Rafael, California, offered coaching in how best to communicate the subtle, careful art of remedy making in a modern laboratory.

Alan Waugh, a shaman at Spirit Wisdom Healing Center near Mt Shasta, California, whose information about Shamanism helped me bring it into a real world perspective.

Luis Tamani, Peruvian artist and shaman, for the use, on the cover, of his powerful painting, *Cuando las plantas Cantan* (When the Plants Sing) luis-tamani.com

Sources

Andrews, Ted. *Animal Speak*. St. Paul MN: Llewellyn Publications, 1993.

Buhner, Stephen Harrod. *Plant Intelligence and the Imaginal Realm*. Rochester VT: Bear and Company, 2014.

Carson, David. *Crossing into Medicine Country*. New York: Arcade Publishing, 2005.

Connor, Nancy, Ed. *Shamans of the World*. Boulder CO: Sounds True, Inc., 2008.

Cowan, Eliot. *Plant Spirit Medicine*. Newberg OR: Swan Raven & Co, 1995.

Fraser, Peter. *Birds: Seeking the Freedom of the Sky*. Ongar, UK: Good News Press, 2009.

Hahnemann, Samuel. *Materia Medica Pura Vol 1.* New Delhi, India: B. Jain Publishers, 1995.

Hahnemann, Samuel. (O'Reilly, Wenda Brewster PhD, ed.) *Organon of the Medical Art*, Redmond WA: Birdcage Books, 1996.

Harner, Michael. *The Way of the Shaman*. San Francisco: Harper, 1990.

Herrick, Nancy. *Animal Minds, Human Voices*. Nevada City CA: Hahnemann Clinic Publishing, 1998.

Herrick, Nancy. *Sacred Plants, Human Voices*. Grass Valley CA: Hahnemann Clinic Publishing, 2003.

Herrick, Nancy Dr. & Morrison, Roger MD. *Miasms of the New Millennium*. Grass Valley CA: Hahnemann Clinic Publishing, 2014.

Kalweit, Holger. *Shamans, Healers, and Medicine Men*. Boston: Shambhala, 2000.

Mangialavori, Massimo. *Fungi (Materia Medica Clinica Volume 2)*. North Charleston, South Carolina: CreateSpace, 2017.

Moss, Robert. *Dreaming the Soul Back Home*. Novato CA: New World Library, 2012.

Pollan, Michel. *How to Change Your Mind*. New York: Penguin Press, 2018.

Rowe, Todd MD, MD(H), CCH, DHt. *The Desert World, A Homeopathic Exploration*. Phoenix AZ: Desert Institute Publishing, 2006.

Sankaran, Rajan. *An Insight into Plants Volumes I and II*. Mumbai, India: Homeopathic Medical Publishers, revised 2005.

Scholten, Jan. *Homeopathy and Minerals*. Netherlands: Stichting Alonnissos, 1993.

Shore, Jonathan MD. Birds: *Homeopathic Remedies from the Avian Realm*. El Cerrito CA: Homeopathy West Publishers, 2004.

Simard, Suzanne. *How Trees Talk To Each Other*. YouTube, August 30, 2016.

Tompkins, Peter and Bird, Christopher. *The Secret Life of Plants*. New York: Harper, 1973.

Villoldo, Alberto. *Shaman, Healer, Sage*. New York: Harmonic Books, 2000.

Vitale, Simone. *Music of the Plants – How It Works*. YouTube, July 14, 2016.

Vithoulkas, George. *Homeopathy: Medicine of the New Man*. New York: Avon Books, 1971.

Walsh, Roger MD, PhD. *The Spirit of Shamanism*. New York: G.P. Putnam's Sons, 1990.

Whitmont, Edward MD. *Psyche and Substance*. Berkeley CA: North Atlantic Books, 1991.

Wohlleben, Peter. *The Hidden Life of Trees*. Ludwig-Verlag, Munich: Greystone Books, 2015.

Index

A

B

Made in the USA
Middletown, DE
25 March 2019